505 BOXING QUESTIONS

YOUR FRIENDS
CAN'T ANSWER

Other books in this series:
505 Baseball Questions Your Friends Can't Answer
(updated and revised)
John Kingston
505 Football Questions Your Friends Can't Answer
(updated and revised)
Harold Rosenthal
505 Hockey Questions Your Friends Can't Answer
Frank Polnaszek
505 Basketball Questions Your Friends Can't Answer
Sol Barzman

and also:

505 Rock 'n' Roll Questions Your Friends Can't Answer
Nicholas and Elizabeth Schaffner

505 BOXING QUESTIONS

YOUR FRIENDS
CAN'T ANSWER

**BERT RANDOLPH SUGAR
AND JOHN GRASSO**

WALKER AND COMPANY
NEW YORK

796.83
S947
A-1

Copyright © 1982 by Bert Randolph Sugar, Sports Collectors Encyclopedia

All rights reserved. No part of this book may be reproduced or transmitted in any form or by any means, electric or mechanical, including photocopying, recording, or by any information storage and retrieval system, without permission in writing from the Publisher.

First published in the United States of America in 1982 by the Walker Publishing Company, Inc.

Published simultaneously in Canada by John Wiley & Sons Canada, Limited, Rexdale, Ontario.

ISBN: 0-8027-0689-4 (cloth)
      0-8027-7180-7 (paperback)
Library of Congress Catalog Card Number: 81-51965

Printed in the United States of America

10 9 8 7 6 5 4 3 2 1

Sugar, Bert Randolph.
   505 boxing questions your friends can't answer.
   1. Boxing—Miscellanea. I. Grasso, John. II. Title. III. Title: Five hundred five boxing questions your friends can't answer.
GV1133.S89   1982   796.8'3   81-51963
ISBN 0-8027-0689-4   AACR2
ISBN 0-8027-7180-7 (pbk.)

Introduction

One snowy evening a few years back, when, like Clement Moore's characters, everyone was "tucked up snug in their beds," our telephone rang. It being three o'clock in the morning, my wife correctly surmised that the call was not for her, and passed the phone quickly over to my side of the bed.

"Hello," said the slightly slurred voice on the other end of the line, sounding as though its owner had already tipped more than one cup of kindness for auld lang syne, "Is this the editor of *Ring* Magazine?" Obviously too befogged by sleep—or the lack-thereof—to deflect what I knew was coming, I admitted it.

Now sure of his quarry, the owner of the voice went on. "In the 1935 match between Jimmy Braddock and Max Baer . . . " here he stopped to punctuate with a gasp for breath, "did it end in a knockout or a deshishion?"

"A decision," I mumbled, all the while thinking only of hanging up, and getting back to the business at hand.

With hardly a word of thanks, the disembodied voice on the other end, looking for all the world like a black telephone, said "Here. Tell my friend."

Now a new voice came over the wires. "Hello, we're calling from Baltimore," it said, as if *that* made a difference. "What wash it," he demanded. "Knockout or deshishion?"

Anger melted my mental daze. "A knockout!" I snapped, and hung up, contemplating the delicious scene now taking place some three hundred miles south between the two barroom triviots who, I hoped, were carrying on their minor disagreement in a more animated mannner until some friendly bartender could retire them to their respective neutral corners.

It has always been thus. For trivia, that six-letter word defined by Webster as "insignificant or inessential matters; trivialities; trifles," has been around almost as long as John Barleycorn himself. And, in that time, has become the barroom's second leading pastime.

Ask any bartender what consumes his patrons the most, instead of the other way around, and without a second thought he will answer "trivia." He may not know the word's exact meaning, but he will know its place in the hierarchy of barroom topics. And the two subjects which most delight, and befuddle, the bar patron are baseball and boxing. They are the two sports with soul—herein defined as history, individual performers and performances, and colorful characters. (Whoever heard of a trivia question about interior linemen? It has always been the contention of this writer that the three surest ways for a wanted fugitive to evade detection are as the vice president of the United States, a captain on a trans-Atlantic cruise, or an interior lineman in the NFL.)

Trivia questions are, by nature, not those you can look up quickly in *The Ring Record Book*—such as "How many knockouts did Joe Louis have?"—but those you-can't-look-'em-up questions that challenge the recollection and the imagination of the questioner and the questionee, like "Who is the only man ever to fight both Joe Louis and Jack Dempsey?"

Boxing, with its endless stream of statistics, lore and legend, unites many of those who follow the sport—factory workers, executives, students, professors, bartenders or just plain ol' patrons—into trivia buffs. Or, more correctly named, triviots. And, in so doing, forges a proud bond between them that few other sports are able to do.

To these boxing fans, as well as to those who helped me in developing these questions—John Grasso, E. J. Gary, Herb Goldman and many others, both known and unknown to me down through the years—I dedicate this book.

As for the ultimate question, from the one I thank most of all, my bemused wife: "Who's interest in all that boxing trivia?" I can only say: We are. We all are!

>Bert Randolph Sugar
>Chappaqua, New York
>November 27, 1981

Contents

Bareknuckles	1
The Heavyweight Champions	8
The Flyweight Champions	23
Other Champions	31
Time Out	48
Names	50
Relatives	58
The Boxing Hall of Fame	63
The Olympic Games	66
Time Out	79
Referees, Managers, Promoters, and Others	83
Places	91
Quotations	98
Writers and Boxing Literature	102
Movies, Television, Radio, and Theater	108
Time Out	116
Scoring	119
The Ring Ratings	122
Odds and Ends	129

Bareknuckles

1. Which American bareknuckle champion was also a U.S. congressman?
2. What boxer took a count of 30 before being knocked out?
3. What British heavyweight champion was born on Boxing Day?
4. Which bareknuckle boxer was "sharkproof"?
5. In the jargon of the London Prize Ring what do these terms mean?
   a. monkey
   b. a Belcher
   c. a bunch of fives
   d. Tom Owen's stop
   e. heavily grassed
   f. in chancery
   g. closed his mince
   h. rallied in prime twig
6. In that same jargon which parts of the body were these?
   a. flipper
   b. gob
   c. smeller
   d. peepers
   e. conk
   f. ogles
   g. mark
   h. nob
7. Boxers in the London Prize Ring were measured in stone. What is a stone?
8. What were the most rounds fought in a bareknuckle bout?

9. What was the longest bareknuckle bout by time?
10. Which bareknuckle boxer engaged in a match on his wedding day?
11. What does "the great glass case of the 1851 Exhibition to a cucumber frame" mean?
12. One American bareknuckle championship claimant, who also bore the name of a golf immortal, was a Civil War spy. Can you name him?
13. Who was the first recognized heavyweight champion?
14. When was the first international bout?
15. For what bout was the first grandstand erected?
16. What bareknuckle boxers were known by these nicknames?
    a. Young Rump Steak
    b. The Deaf 'Un
    c. Gay Bristol Boy
    d. The Tinman
    e. The Game Chicken
    f. The Nonpareil
    g. The Chelsea Snob
    h. Bendigo
    i. Death
    j. The Tipton Slasher
    k. The Stalybridge Infant
    l. The Commissary of the Ring
17. Who was the first black boxer to achieve prominence?
18. What bareknuckle heavyweight champion served time in debtor's prison and later became a member of Parliament?
19. In how many states of the United States was prizefighting legal in 1880?
20. What bareknuckle heavyweight champion became a Methodist minister after his retirement from the ring?

21. One of the largest boxers ever was bareknuckle fighter Charles Freeman. How big was he?

22. Which bareknuckle champion was known as the "Father of Boxing"?

23. The second heavyweight champion was a man named George Taylor, a relative unknown. He overcame a substantial handicap. What was it?

ANSWERS

1. John Morrissey won the American heavyweight championship by defeating John C. Heenan in 11 rounds in 1858. He then retired from the ring and operated luxurious gambling houses in New York City and Saratoga, thru which he made a large fortune. He became a prominent figure in New York politics and served two terms in Congress.

2. Any boxer who engaged in a bareknuckle bout under the London Prize Ring rules was automatically given 30 seconds to be revived from the time that he was knocked down. A round lasted until one of the contestants fell, was pushed, or otherwise knocked off his feet.

3. In England, December 26 is celebrated as Boxing Day—a day in which boxes containing gifts are exchanged. Jem Ward, champion from 1822 to 1831, was born on this day in 1800.

4. Peter Jackson, the black Australian whom John L. Sullivan refused to fight, was considered to be "sharkproof." Jackson was a native of St. Croix in the West Indies and when he was twelve years old and swimming in the sea, a shark surfaced near him and turned upon its side to attack. A yard or so from Peter the fish stopped, swam around him and then streaked for the open sea. The only explanation for this was that he was "sharkproof". Only one other man among the 5,000 inhabitants of the island possessed that gift. The two would often swim together without fear in the shark-infested waters.

5. a. left hand
   b. a dark blue handkerchief with white spots, named after Jem Belcher, who always carried a "bird's-eye wipe."
   c. a fist
   d. the act of holding an opponent's arm to prevent him from hitting. This was allowed under early prize ring rules.
   e. felled to the ground
   f. a fighter's head held tightly under one arm by his opponent who uses his free hand to pummel his victim's head.
   g. caused his eye to swell.
   h. made a sprightly recovery

ANSWERS Bareknuckles

6. a. hand
   b. mouth
   c. nose
   d. eyes
   e. nose
   f. eyes
   g. the pit of the stomach
   h. head

7. A stone is a British unit of weight totaling 14 pounds.

8. In 1825 in Cheshire, England, Jack Jones defeated Patsy Tunney in 276 rounds.

9. James Kelly and Jonathan Smith for 6 hours and 15 minutes in Australia in 1855.

10. Harry Jones, known as "The Gay Sailor Boy," on the day he was married, rushed away on foot immediately after the ceremony to keep an appointment in the ring with Jem Aldridge. He arrived panting, jumped into the ring and, in 12 minutes, won the bout and the sum of 5 pounds.

11. "A horse to a hen" and "Lombard Street to a china orange" are phrases used for figurative bets in regard to a certainty. "The great glass case of the 1851 Exhibition to a cucumber frame" was also used by nineteenth-century British boxing writers to indicate a one-sided bet.

12. Ben Hogan, born Benediel Hagen in Wurttemberg, Germany, was an American heavyweight title claimant in 1872. He was both a Union and a Confederate spy during the Civil War, as well as an oil magnate, theatrical producer, and gambling house operator during his lifetime.

13. James Figg, the only heavyweight champion born in the seventeenth century, claimed the heavyweight championship in 1719. He opened a boxing academy called Figg's Amphitheatre. In addition to his boxing skills, he was also an accomplished swordsman and cudgel expert.

14. On April 17, 1860, John Carmel Heenan, known as "The Benecia Boy," the American heavyweight champion, fought Tom Sayers, the English champion, at Farnborough, England. The bout lasted 2 hours and 20 minutes over 42 rounds and was declared a draw when

[6]   505 BOXING QUESTIONS

the crowd broke into the ring at a time when Heenan seemed to be winning. Alan Lloyd's book The Great Prize Fight is an excellent account of this bout.

15. The first grandstand ever erected for a boxing match was built for the bout between Tom Spring and Jack Langan, held January 7, 1824, in the outskirts of Worcester, England, seating about 4,000. The people who bought a seat paid 10 shillings. The stands were packed and more than 20,000 stood to view the fight.

16. **a.** Peter Crawley (his father was a butcher)
     b. James Burke
     c. Cy Davis
     d. Bill Hickman
     e. Henry Pearce (from Hen—short for Henry)
     f. Jack Randall (Jack Dempsey, the middleweight, also used this name)
     g. Alec Reid
     h. William Thompson
     i. Stephen Oliver
     j. William Perry
     k. Sam Hurst
     l. Tom Oliver

17. Bill Richmond (The Black Terror) went to England in 1777 with General Earl Percy, one of the commanders of British forces then occupying New York; Richmond had frequently beaten English soldiers in fights privately held for the general's friends' amusement in New York. In England, Richmond knocked out several top boxers but was defeated by Tom Cribb, who later became heavyweight champion.

The second black bareknuckle boxer to achieve prominence was Tom Molineaux of Richmond, Virginia. Molineaux gained some repute as a boxer in America, but achieved his greatest success in England. He lost to Cribb in 1810 when Cribb was heavyweight champion.

18. John Gully, son of a Bristol butcher, was in a debtor's prison when Henry Pearce, the heavyweight champion, paid him a visit. Gully had some reputation as a boxer and Pearce sparred with him in his jail quarters. Gully made such a good showing that the news went abroad and a British sportsman named Fletcher Reid paid Gully's debts, had him discharged from custody and matched him against

ANSWERS Bareknuckles

Pearce on October 8, 1805. Gully lost in 64 rounds in 1 hour and 17 minutes. When Pearce retired, Gully was universally recognized as his successor to the title.

Gully later became wealthy and in 1832, as the result of a bet, he became a candidate for Parliament and was elected. He served two terms and then resigned.

19. Prizefighting was illegal in 38 states in 1880. It was legal in no states. There were only 38 states at that time.

20. Bendigo, heavyweight champion from 1839 to 1840 and 1845 to 1850, had been imprisoned 28 times for breaking the peace as a result of his ring battles. While in prison he was moved by a sermon delivered by a prison chaplain and upon his release began a new career as a evangelist.

21. Charles Freeman battled 70 rounds with William Perry in 1842 before the bout was stopped by police. The battle was resumed ten days later and Perry was awarded the decision on a foul after 37 more rounds.

Freeman stood 6 feet 10½ inches and weighed 276 pounds to Perry's 6 feet ½ inch and 185 pounds.

22. Jack Broughton, the third heavyweight champion, drew up the first set of rules. These were the foundation for the Marquess of Queensberry rules. Broughton was champion for 21 years and lived to the age of 85.

23. George Taylor was blind in one eye and lost his championship when he was blinded in the other.

The Heavyweight Champions

1. Which heavyweight champion had the most bouts in his career?
2. Which heavyweight champion had the fewest bouts in his career?
3. Name the man who lost the most heavyweight championship bouts.
4. Which heavyweight champ had the most consecutive knockouts?
5. Only one heavyweight champion had six successful title defenses by knockout in one year. Who was he?
6. Who boxed the most consecutive heavyweight championship bouts that went 15 rounds to a decision?
7. What heavyweight title holder boxed the fewest rounds in heavyweight championship bouts?
8. When was the last heavyweight championship bout that was scheduled for more than 15 rounds?
9. One heavyweight champion boxed a three-round exhibition at the age of 67. Name him.
10. Name the only undisputed heavyweight title holders never to lose a decision or box to a draw during their professional career.
11. Which heavyweight champ fought the most consecutive successful title defenses outside the United States?

THE HEAVYWEIGHT CHAMPIONS

12. Can you name the heavyweight champion who won three consecutive title bouts in the first round?
13. One boxer fought for the heavyweight title even though he had been previously knocked out 16 times in his career. What is his name?
14. There once was a heavyweight title bout in which it was a sure bet that Johnson would be the winner. Why?
15. Only one heavyweight champion won the title on his birthday. Can you name him?
16. Two heavyweight champions had the same birthday and also met each other for the championship. Who were they?
17. In which heavyweight title fight was the last round fought two months after the first round?
18. Who was the only man to meet both Muhammad Ali and Rocky Marciano in the ring?
19. Which heavyweight champion's professional boxing career spanned the most years?
20. Bob Fitzsimmons, at 167 pounds, was the lightest man to win the heavyweight championship. Who was the second lightest man to do so?
21. Who was the heaviest unsuccessful challenger for the heavyweight title?
22. Name the heavyweight "white hope" champion who killed an opponent in a one-round knockout and then lost 14 of his next 15 bouts, including 12 by knockout.
23. Which heavyweight champion went more than four years without defending his title?
24. A heavyweight champion once attracted 23,322 fans and grossed $74,200 for an exhibition. Can you name him?
25. Who is the only fighter to lose three consecutive heavyweight title bouts?

26. In which heavyweight championship bout did both men weigh less than the light heavyweight limit of 175 pounds?

27. List the heavyweight champions who have the same names as major league baseball players.

28. What is the longest span of time without a heavyweight championship bout that went the scheduled distance?

29. Do you know who is the only heavyweight champion who never won a heavyweight championship bout?

30. When were there three consecutive heavyweight championship bouts in which a new champion was crowned?

31. Which heavyweight champ received the first $1,000,000 check for a championship bout?

32. What, besides the amount, was unusual about this check?

33. The longest heavyweight championship bout to a decision and the quickest knockout in a heavyweight championship bout occurred in consecutive bouts. Who were the participants?

34. Through 1980, has there ever been a heavyweight championship in which both men weighed the same? If so, when did it take place and who were the participants?

35. Two heavyweight champions have attended college. Who were they?

36. Holley Mims, middleweight contender during the 1950s, defeated which future heavyweight champion?

37. List the light heavyweight champions who outweighed their opponents in a heavyweight championship bout.

38. From 1892 to 1980, what percentage of heavyweight championship bouts lasted more than 10 rounds?

39. One heavyweight champion boxed more heavyweight championship rounds than 11 other heavyweight champions combined. Name him.

THE HEAVYWEIGHT CHAMPIONS [11]

40. Name the man who boxed more rounds in heavyweight championship bouts than 15 heavyweight champions but never won the heavyweight title.

41. What heavyweight champion was outweighed in every one of his 13 heavyweight championship bouts?

42. List the only heavyweight champs who didn't compete in a heavyweight championship bout that went the scheduled distance.

43. Which of the following heavyweight champions scored the most knockouts in heavyweight championship bouts: Max Baer, Primo Carnera, Jimmy Ellis, Ingemar Johansson, Archie Moore, Ken Norton, Floyd Patterson, Max Schmeling, Jack Sharkey, Leon Spinks, Ernest Terrell, John Tate, Gene Tunney, Jess Willard, or Jersey Joe Walcott?

44. Only one man who competed in more than one heavyweight championship bout went the distance in every one. What is his name?

45. Who was the only challenger for the heavyweight championship against two different champions within six months?

46. Which heavyweight king never fought a preliminary bout?

47. Name the only heavyweight champions to lose their titles in their first defense.

48. List the sparring partners of Muhammad Ali who later became heavyweight champions.

49. Muhammad Ali recieved $2,000 for his first professional bout. How much did he receive for his second professional bout?

50. Five heavyweight champions did not defend their title for periods of more than three years. Who are they?

51. The first million-dollar gate was the Dempsey-Carpentier match in 1921. Ringside tickets for that event were priced at $50. The first Dempsey-Tunney bout in 1926 set a new record

for receipts at $1,895,733. How much were ringside tickets for that bout?

52. A judge named Fake played what role in the Braddock-Louis heavyweight championship bout?

53. What heavyweight champion won 11 consecutive bouts by knockout after losing the championship?

54. Who is the only heavyweight champion to have a lifetime won-lost percentage of less than .700?

55. It is well known that Rocky Marciano defeated Joe Louis in Louis's last professional bout. But who was the last man that Louis defeated?

56. Which heavyweight champion started boxing professionally at the age of 29?

57. Who was the only man to knock out Jack Dempsey?

58. In what heavyweight championship bout was the champion knocked down 11 times in 11 rounds?

59. Joe Louis ended the ring careers of which five boxers?

60. Two heavyweight champions never competed in a bout lasting more than 12 rounds. Who are they?

61. Who was the only man to box Joe Louis and Jack Dempsey in a regular bout?

62. What future heavyweight champ boxed in the preliminary to the Dempsey-Carpentier fight?

63. A scheduled heavyweight championship bout was once called off by a member of the President's Cabinet. Who were the scheduled participants?

64. Who is the only heavyweight champion to lose in a bid for the light heavyweight title?

65. Which heavyweight champ scored the most one-round knockouts?

THE HEAVYWEIGHT CHAMPIONS

66. Which heavyweight champion since Jack Dempsey scored the fewest one-round knockouts?

67. Two heavyweight champions are buried within 200 feet of each other. What are their names?

68. Only three men have won the Olympic heavyweight gold medals and boxed in world heavyweight championship bouts. Who were they?

ANSWERS

1. *Ezzard Charles had 122 bouts, of which he won 96, drew 1, and lost 25. He won the NBA version of the heavyweight crown in his seventieth bout and the undisputed title in his seventy-fourth. Only eight other heavyweight champions had as many as 70 bouts in their lifetimes and only Primo Carnera and Jack Johnson had more than 100.*

2. *Jim Corbett had only 19 bouts that were not classified as exhibitions. He won 11, lost 4, drew 2 and had 2 bouts that were declared no contest. Leon Spinks, who won the title in his eighth bout, is still active but has only 14 bouts through 1980.*

3. *Jersey Joe Walcott was defeated twice by Joe Louis and twice by Ezzard Charles before defeating Charles for the crown. Walcott successfully defended against Charles but then lost the title to Rocky Marciano and lost again in a rematch with Marciano. His record in heavyweight championship bouts was 2 wins and 6 losses.*

4. *Joe Louis' best streak was only 10. Floyd Patterson, Joe Frazier, and Sonny Liston each had 11. Rocky Marciano had 16 and Primo Carnera had 18. George Foreman, from March 31, 1970, until his defeat by Muhammad Ali in Zaire on October 30, 1974, scored 24 straight knockouts for the all-time record among heavyweight champions.*

5. *Tommy Burns in 1908 successfully defended his title six straight times by knockout before being defeated by Jack Johnson in Sydney, Australia. Burns had had two previous knockouts in 1907 for a total of eight consecutive knockouts in heavyweight title defenses, the record for the heavyweight division (since tied by Larry Holmes).*

Joe Louis had seven successful title defenses in 1941, the most by any heavyweight champion in one year, but after winning four by knockout, he defeated Buddy Baer by disqualification and then won two more by knockout. Louis also had two streaks of seven consecutive knockout defenses separated by a 15-round decision over Arturo Godoy in 1940.

6. *Muhammad Ali from 1976 to 1978 defeated Ken Norton, Alfredo Evangelista, and Earnie Shavers by decision before losing to Leon Spinks. He then defeated Spinks in a rematch by decision for a total of five consecutive 15-round heavyweight championship bouts, fought to a decision.*

ANSWERS The Heavyweight Champions

7. Charles (Sonny) Liston gave boxing fans less for their money than any other heavyweight champion. He fought in four heavyweight championship bouts but only completed six rounds. Three of the four bouts did not go past the first round. In the other bout he did not come out for the seventh round. He was in action a grand total of 23 minutes and 58 seconds in the four bouts.

8. On March 21, 1941, Joe Louis stopped Abe Simon in the thirteenth round of a scheduled 20-round bout in Detroit. Louis knocked out Bob Pastor in the eleventh round of a 20-rounder on September 20, 1939, also in Detroit.

9. Jack Johnson, aged 67, boxed Joe Jeannette, aged 66, in a three-round exhibition in New York on November 27, 1945.

10. John L. Sullivan never lost a decision but did box to three draws. Bob Fitzsimmons also never lost a decision but had one draw and five no-decision bouts. Jim Jeffries had two draws. Joe Louis, Sonny Liston, Joe Frazier and George Foreman also lost only 1 decision each.

Rocky Marciano won all 49 of his bouts and was the only undefeated heavyweight champion, but Ingemar Johansson also never lost a decision or had a draw in his brief career. He had only 28 professional bouts and won all but the two in which he was knocked out by Floyd Patterson.

11. Tommy Burns holds the record with seven consecutive title defenses in 1907-08 in London, Dublin, Paris, Sydney and Melbourne before losing his title to Jack Johnson in Sydney in 1908. Muhammad Ali had four bouts outside the United States in 1966 and Jack Johnson had three bouts abroad in 1913-14.

12. There have been only 13 one-round knockouts in heavyweight championship bouts. Joe Louis had five, including three in a row against Max Schmeling, John Henry Lewis, and Jack Roper—a total of 6 minutes and 53 seconds in 1938-39.

13. Lee Oma, with a record of 62-26-4, was given a shot at Ezzard Charles's title in 1951, putting up a battle for ten rounds before being stopped.

14. When Jack Johnson met Battling Jim Johnson in Paris on December 19, 1913, it seemed to be a sure thing that Johnson (one of them) would be the winner. But if you had made that bet you still wouldn't have won, as Jack Johnson claimed he had broken his arm and the referee declared the bout a draw after ten rounds.

15. George Foreman celebrated his twenty-fifth birthday on January 22, 1973, by defeating Joe Frazier in Kingston, Jamaica, for the heavyweight championship.

16. Jack Sharkey, born on October 26, 1902, and Primo Carnera, born four years later to the day, met on June 29, 1933. Carnera stopped Sharkey in the sixth round to win the heavyweight title. Ironically, Carnera died exactly 34 years later on June 29, 1967.

James J. Corbett and Rocky Marciano also shared the same birthday, September 1, although they were born 57 years apart.

17. In the Jim Jeffries-Tom Sharkey heavyweight championship bout at the Coney Island Athletic Club in 1899, 25 tough rounds were fought with Jeffries retaining his crown in a close decision. The bout was filmed for later showing in movie theaters. The company that bought the movie rights failed to apply for a copyright and a rival organization was soon showing a bootlegged version of the fight. It was decided, two months after the original bout, to refilm the last round of the fight in order to have a different product and qualify for a copyright. The original ringside conditions were reproduced as accurately as possible, the Coney Island AC was again used and fans were brought in to provide a crowd background. Referee George Siler was not available, so Jeffries' manager, William Brady, impersonated him by borrowing a black slouch hat and wearing a false moustache. It wasn't necessary for Sharkey to do any making-up to simulate a fighter who had received a severe beating—after two months his body was still black and blue from the original battle.

The film was made, the copyright received, and the bootleg film was no longer a source of trouble.

18. Archie Moore was knocked out by Rocky Marciano in the ninth round of their heavyweight championship bout in 1955. Moore was again stopped in four by Ali (then known as Cassius Clay) in 1962.

19. Bob Fitzsimmons's first recorded ring appearance was in 1880 at the age of 17, as an amateur. He continued boxing until 1909 and came out of retirement in 1914 to box two matches at the age of 50, 34 years after his first bout. In order for Muhammad Ali to equal Fitzsimmons's record, he would still have to be boxing professionally in 1991.

20. Jim Corbett only weighed 178 pounds when he defeated John L. Sullivan in 1892 for the crown. Corbett gave away 34 pounds to Sullivan but stopped him in the twenty-first round. Bat Masterson was

ANSWERS *The Heavyweight Champions*

the timekeeper for that bout, which was part of the three-day Carnival of Champions in New Orleans.

21. Abe Simon twice challenged Joe Louis unsuccessfully. He weighed 254½ to Louis's 202 in 1941 and lasted 13 rounds. The following year he gained three quarters of a pound and weighed in at 255½, but this time lasted only 6 rounds. Primo Carnera weighed 260½ pounds when he successfully challenged Jack Sharkey and won the title in 1933. Carnera later weighed in at 270 pounds for his defense against Tommy Loughran, who gave away 86 pounds but still lasted 15 rounds.

22. Arthur Pelkey, a top heavyweight contender during Jack Johnson's reign as champion, was matched with Luther McCarty for the "white hope" championship in Calgary in 1913. McCarty died 8 minutes after an apparently light blow had been delivered in a clinch during the first round of that bout. McCarty's death was due to a brain hemorrhage and was probably caused by a previous injury. Nevertheless, Pelkey was never the same after that bout and did not box again for nearly a year. He continued competing until 1920, but never won another bout.

23. Joe Louis was one of the most active champions of all time and defended his title 25 times—more than any other champion. Yet after his title defense against Abe Simon on March 27, 1942, he did not engage in another championship bout until June 19, 1946, when he defended against Billy Conn. Louis spent most of that time in the U.S. Army, and boxed several exhibitions during those years.

24. Jack Dempsey boxed a four-round exhibition with King Levinsky at the Chicago Coliseum on February 18, 1932, and drew a crowd of 23,322 paid admissions for a gross of $74,199.94. This is the largest amount ever grossed solely from an exhibition. Dempsey received $33,000 and Levinsky received $11,000. This was more than Dempsey received when he won the heavyweight title.

25. Jersey Joe Walcott, who lost the most heavyweight championship bouts, is also the only man to lose 3 consecutive heavyweight championship bouts. He lost twice to Joe Louis in 1947 and 1948 and then faced Ezzard Charles for Louis's vacated title in 1949, losing for the third straight time.

26. On November 28, 1906, Tommy Burns, the heavyweight champion, faced Philadelphia Jack O'Brien, the light heavyweight champion. Since Burns weighed only 172 and O'Brien 163½, the winner could rightfully have claimed both titles. The bout, however, resulted in a 20-round draw. The referee for that bout was ex-champion Jim Jeffries and he outweighed each of the two boxers by more than 50 pounds.

27. There have been major league baseball players named John L. Sullivan, Tommy Burns, James Ellis, and Joe Frazier. Of the four names only the two players named Burns ever achieved a measure of fame. An infielder for the Chicago Cubs in the nineteenth century named Tommy Burns lasted 13 years and had a lifetime batting average of .264. A second Thomas Burns, known as Oyster Burns, was an outfielder with five teams in the nineteenth century and played for 11 years with a lifetime average of .300.

Joe Frazier was primarily a pinch hitter for the St. Louis Cardinals in the early 1950s and later briefly managed the New York Mets. Jim Ellis appeared in ten games as a pitcher in 1967 and 1969. There were five John Sullivans, but only one John L. Sullivan. He played the outfield for the Braves and the Cubs in 1920-21.

28. On June 17, 1954, Rocky Marciano won a unanimous 15-round decision over Ezzard Charles. From then until March 5, 1965, every one of the 15 heavyweight championship bouts ended short of the 15-round distance. On that date, a bout between Ernest Terrell and Eddie Machen was held that went the 15-round distance and Terrell, the winner, was recognized by the WBA as the heavyweight champion.

29. Ken Norton was acclaimed heavyweight champion by the WBC when Leon Spinks declined to meet him before Spinks's return bout with Muhammad Ali. Norton lost his first bout in defense of his "title" to Larry Holmes. Norton had also lost in two prior bids for the title against George Foreman and Muhammad Ali, making him a heavyweight champion with an 0-3 record in heavyweight championship bouts.

30. Between the reigns of Tunney and Louis, the heavyweight title changed hands with almost every bout. After Tunney retired in 1928, there were nine championship bouts from 1930 to 1937, and in six of them a new champion was crowned. In 1934, Max Baer defeated Primo Carnera. In 1935, Jim Braddock defeated Baer, and in his first defense two years later, Braddock lost to Joe Louis. The law of averages then came into play and for the next 12 years Louis remained as the only heavyweight champion.

ANSWERS The Heavyweight Champions [19]

31. Gene Tunney received a check for $1,000,000 for his share as champion in his second bout with Jack Dempsey. The bout drew 104,943 spectators at Soldiers Field, Chicago, with gross receipts of $2,658,660.

32. Tunney was not entitled to $1,000,000 as his share in the bout. His share amounted to only $990,445, but he wanted to receive a check for a million dollars and wrote his own check to Tex Rickard, the promoter, for the difference.

33. Jim Jeffries boxed 25 rounds with Tom Sharkey on November 3, 1899, and was awarded the decision of the referee (see question 17). For Jeffries's next defense on April 6, 1900, he apparently didn't want to spend any more time in the ring than necessary and knocked out Jack Finnegan in 55 seconds of the first round.

34. No. But there have been five bouts in which the participants weighed within one quarter pound of each other. They were Louis-Braddock, Louis-Nova, Marciano-LaStarza, Marciano-Moore and Ali-Terrell.

35. Ken Norton and John L. Sullivan.

36. Holley Mims was a top-ranked middleweight from 1948 to 1967 who often appeared on television and always gave a good account of himself, but was never fortunate enough to get a title shot. Among his victories during his 20-year career was one over Jimmy Ellis in 1961.

37. Archie Moore outweighed Floyd Patterson by 5½ pounds (187¾ to 182¼) when they met in 1956. Gus Lesnevich weighed 182 to Ezzard Charles's 180 in 1949, although Lesnevich was no longer light heavyweight champion at the time.

38. Of the 164 bouts for the heavyweight championship from 1892 to 1980, 73 bouts, or 45%, lasted more than 10 rounds. Eight of these 73 also lasted more than 15 rounds.

39. Muhammad Ali appeared in 25 heavyweight championship bouts and boxed 255 complete rounds. This is more complete rounds heavyweight championship bouts than Sonny Liston, George Foreman, Ingemar Johansson, Jack Sharkey, Gene Tunney, Bob Fitzsimmons, Ken Norton, Marvin Hart, Max Schmeling, Jim Braddock, and Max Baer combined boxed.

40. Philadelphia Jack O'Brien challenged for the heavyweight title three times. He boxed a 20-round draw with Tommy Burns, lost a 20-

round decision to Burns and boxed a six-round no-decision bout with Jack Johnson for a total of 46 rounds of heavyweight championship action. The 11 boxers mentioned in the previous answer all had less than 46 rounds of heavyweight championship bouts, as did Primo Carnera, Jimmy Ellis, Leon Spinks, John Tate, and Jess Willard. John L. Sullivan also only boxed 20-plus rounds in heavyweight championship bouts under Marquess of Queensberry rules.

41. Floyd Patterson weighed between 182 and 196¾ pounds for his 13 heavyweight championship bouts, but regardless of his weight, his opponent always weighed more. No other heavyweight champion who engaged in more than three title bouts was outweighed in all of them.

42. Mike Weaver, George Foreman, Sonny Liston, Ingemar Johansson, Bob Fitzsimmons, and Jim Corbett all never fought a heavyweight championship bout that went the distance.

43. The amazing answer to this question is that Floyd Patterson scored more knockouts in heavyweight championship bouts than the other 14 champions combined! He scored eight knockouts while none of the others scored more than one.

44. Ernest Terrell boxed in four heavyweight championship bouts, each of which resulted in a 15-round decision.

45. George Chuvalo lost a 15-round decision to Ernest Terrell in November, 1965, and lost a 15-round decision to Muhammad Ali in March, 1966.

46. Joe Louis was a Golden Gloves champion as an amateur and his first professional bout was a main event, as were all his subsequent bouts.

47. Bob Fitzsimmons, Jack Sharkey, Max Baer, Jim Braddock, Ingemar Johansson, Ken Norton, Leon Spinks, and John Tate were all unable to successfully defend their championships. Fitzsimmons and Johansson also failed in rematch bids.

48. Both Jimmy Ellis and Larry Holmes were once sparring partners of Muhammad Ali.

49. Ali received only $200 for his second professional bout with Herb Siler in Miami Beach on December 27, 1960. This was Siler's second professional bout as well.

50. Jim Corbett, Jess Willard, Jack Dempsey, Joe Louis, and Muhammad Ali were all inactive for periods of three or more years during

ANSWERS The Heavyweight Champions [21]

their reigns as heavyweight champions. Louis's and Ali's inactivity were involuntary—the result of the U.S. government.

51. Only $27.50. Compared to many other heavyweight championships, those tickets were one of the ring's greatest bargains. Today, a ringside ticket from that bout would probably bring more than $27.50 as a collector's item.

52. Since they were not promoting the fight, Madison Square Garden attempted to get an injunction to prevent the Louis-Braddock bout, claiming that they had an exclusive services contract with Jim Braddock. A Federal Judge named Guy L. Fake denied the Garden's application for a temporary injunction to restrain Braddock from meeting Louis in the ring. In essence, Fake allowed the bout to take place.

53. Although Charles (Sonny) Liston only scored 2 knockouts in his first 9 bouts, he won 37 of the last 45 in his career by knockout, including 11 straight KO victories after his second loss to Muhammad Ali.

54. Only James J. Braddock won less than 70% of his bouts and his lifetime record of 44-22-5 with 12 no-decisions and 2 no-contests was not that bad either. He had a won-lost percentage of .667.

55. Joe Louis defeated Jimmy Bivins by decision on August 15, 1951. Bivins was the top-rated heavyweight contender while Louis was in the service, but never got a chance at Louis' title. He finally was matched with Louis during Louis' comeback attempt.

56. Jess Willard's first recorded bout was in 1911. He was born in 1881. Tommy Burns was also born in 1881 and had been boxing for 11 years before Willard's first bout.

57. Jack Dempsey was only knocked out once in his life. On February 13, 1917, Fireman Jim Flynn floored him for the count in the first round. A year and a day later, Dempsey KO'ed Flynn in one round.

58. Max Baer knocked Primo Carnera down 11 times before the bout was stopped in the eleventh round.

59. Paulino Uzcudun (1935), Jack Sharkey (1936), John Henry Lewis (1939), Buddy Baer (1942), and Abe Simon (1942) all fought their last bouts against Joe Louis and were all knocked out.

60. Both Sonny Liston and George Foreman only boxed one bout in their careers that lasted as many as 12 rounds. Liston defeated Eddie

Machen in a 12-round decision before he became champion and Foreman lost a 12-round decision to Jimmy Young after he had lost his title.

61. Only Jack Sharkey boxed regular matches against both Dempsey and Louis, but after Dempsey retired he went on exhibition tours in 1931 and 1932 and met several men who later boxed Louis. He boxed exhibitions against Jack Roper, Buck Everett, Jack O'Dowd, and King Levinsky—all men who were later knocked out by Louis.

62. Gene Tunney knocked out Soldier Jones in the seventh round of their preliminary bout on July 2, 1921. Dempsey knocked out Carpentier in the fourth.

63. Mike Jacobs scheduled a rematch between Sergeant Joe Louis and Private Billy Conn for Columbus Day, 1942, with the proceeds going to the Army Emergency Relief Fund. But Secretary of War Henry Stimson declared that the bout was "not in the national interest" and ordered it to be cancelled.

64. James J. Braddock lost a 15-round decision for the light heavyweight title to Tommy Loughran in 1929—six years before Braddock won the heavyweight title.

65. Jack Dempsey won 49 of 80 bouts by knockout—25 of the 49 were one-round KOs. Dempsey also scored at least 37 one-round knockouts in exhibiton bouts.

66. Muhammad Ali is one of four heavyweight champions since Jack Dempsey to score only two one-round knockouts. Ingemar Johansson, Jack Sharkey, and Ken Norton are also only credited with two. Jess Willard, Jim Jeffries, and Marvin Hart each have only 1 recorded one-round KO.

67. Bob Fitzsimmons and Jack Johnson are buried within 200 feet of each other in Chicago's Graceland cemetery. Fitzsimmons's name was misspelled on his headstone for more than 50 years, but with the help of the Veteran Boxers Association of Illinois a new headstone was obtained.

68. Only Joe Frazier, George Foreman, and Pete Rademacher won Olympic heavyweight gold medals and competed in world heavyweight bouts. Floyd Patterson won the 1952 middleweight gold medal, Cassius Clay (Muhammad Ali) won the 1960 light heavyweight gold medal, and Leon Spinks won the 1976 light heavyweight gold medal. Ingemar Johansson was the heavyweight runnerup in 1952 and John Tate came in third as a heavyweight in the 1976 Olympic Games.

The Flyweight Champions

1. What flyweight champion was a grandfather at the time he held the title?
2. One flyweight champion lost his title and then failed in five attempts to regain it before succeeding. Who was he?
3. Which flyweight champ won 11 consecutive 15-round bouts?
4. Who was the flyweight champion who had a better knockout percentage than Jack Dempsey?
5. What flyweight champion scored more knockouts than any heavyweight champion?
6. Which flyweight champion had a knockout percentage of .060?
7. There was a flyweight champion who lost almost as many bouts as he won. Can you name him?
8. Who was the first Japanese world champion at any weight?
9. Name the first Thai world champion of any weight.
10. As of 1980, how many flyweight champions had better than 50% knockout percentages?
11. Which flyweight king retired to attend college?
12. What flyweight champion boxed 16 draws in his career?
13. Name two flyweight champions with the same last name.
14. Who was the first African world flyweight champion?

15. What flyweight champ won seven non-title bouts in which his title was at stake?
16. Who was the flyweight champion who lost three of his first four bouts?
17. Which flyweight champion lost in four bids for the title before winning the championship?
18. What flyweight champ met a future welterweight champion in his third professional bout?
19. Name the flyweight champion who defeated two bantamweight champions and three featherweight champions but failed in two bids for the featherweight title?
20. Which flyweight champion died of an infected tooth?
21. Who is the only flyweight champion to win the bantamweight championship, as of 1980?
22. One flyweight champion was knocked out ten times in his career. Who was he?
23. Who was the first flyweight champion to regain the flyweight title?
24. What else was noteworthy about that achievement?
25. What flyweight title bout ended in a disqualification when the boxing commission ruled that one contestant illegally used sugar water between rounds?
26. Which flyweight champion held the title for only 47 days?
27. Name the flyweight champion who was knocked down 18 times in one bout.
28. A flyweight champion once received $160,000 to his challenger's $10,000 in a title bout. Can you name the men involved?
29. Who boxed for the WBC Junior Flyweight championship in his first professional bout?

THE FLYWEIGHT CHAMPIONS

30. What junior flyweight successfully defended his title 11 times in two years?

31. Which flyweight champ would burst into song following his bouts?

32. What flyweight champion boxed 43 consecutive bouts of 10 or 12 rounds?

33. Name the flyweight champ who held three wins over a future lightweight champion

34. One flyweight champion knocked out Billy Papke and fought a 10-round no-decision bout with Jack Sharkey. Who was he?

35. There has only been one flyweight championship bout held outdoors in New York City. When was it and who were the participants?

36. What flyweight was the first man to defend four titles successfully in a single bout?

ANSWERS

1. *Hawaiian-born Salvador (Dado) Marino was one month shy of his thirty-fourth birthday when he won the championship in 1950. He held the title for nearly two years and during that time became a grandfather, at the age of 36.*

2. *Shoji Oguma provides a good model for the adage "try, try again." He was WBC flyweight champion from 1974 to 1975 and then lost to Alfonso Lopez, to Miguel Canto twice, drew with Betulio Gonzalez, and was knocked out by Gonzalez in WBA and WBC championship bouts from 1976 to 1979. On May 18, 1980, in his sixth attempt at regaining the title, he was successful, stopping Chan-Hee Park in the ninth round.*

3. *Miguel Canto won the flyweight title from Shoji Oguma in 1975. Although obviously not possessing a knockout punch, he defended his crown successfully 14 times—more than any other flyweight champion. After winning a 10-round nontitle bout in 1976, he won 11 consecutive bouts, all of which were championship bouts that went the 15-round distance. No boxer in any other weight class has ever duplicated this feat.*

4. *Jack Dempsey knocked out .613 of his opponents (49 in 80 bouts). Pascual Perez of Argentina, flyweight champion from 1954 to 1960, knocked out 56 of his 91 opponents for a .615 percentage. More than one half of the heavyweight champions have lower knockout percentages than Perez.*

5. *Jimmy Wilde, flyweight champion from 1916 to 1923, competed in 140 recorded bouts and knocked out 77 opponents for a percentage of .550. The most knockouts by any heavyweight champion in his career is the 68 scored by Primo Carnera, followed by Ezzard Charles's 58.*

6. *At the other end of the knockout spectrum is flyweight Corporal Izzy Schwartz, whose punches couldn't hurt a fly. He stopped only 7 of 117 opponents for a knockout percentage of .060, although he did manage to score two knockouts in consecutive bouts in August, 1928.*

7. *Bernabe Villacampo of the Philippines won only 6 more bouts than he lost from 1963 to 1979 as he compiled a record of 23-17-1. Surprisingly, he did not receive even a single vote in* The Ring's *poll to*

ANSWERS The Flyweight Champions [27]

select the worst champions of all time, although 17 other flyweight champions did.

8. Yoshio Shirai knocked out flyweight champion Dado Marino in a nontitle bout in Honolulu in 1951 and was rewarded with a rematch in May, 1952 in which he again defeated Marino and won the title. Shirai became the first Japanese to win a world championship. He successfully defended his crown four times before losing it to Pascual Perez in November, 1954. From 1954 to 1980 there have been more flyweight champions who were Japanese than any other nationality. More than a dozen world champions in all weight classes have been Japanese.

9. Thailand never had a world champion boxer until Pone Kingpetch defeated Pascual Perez for the flyweight title in 1960.

10. In addition to Pascual Perez, there have been seven flyweight champions who have knocked out more than half of their opponents: Guty Espadas, Jimmy Wilde, Peter Kane, Efren Torres, Venice Borkorsor, Betulio Gonzalez and Tae-shik Kim.

11. After winning the Olympic championship in 1924 and the world flyweight championship in 1927, Fidel La Barba announced his retirement from the ring at the age of 22 to attend Stanford University.

12. Valentin Angelmann and Victor (Young) Perez each recorded 16 draws in their careers. They met once and Perez won the decision.

13. Victor (Young) Perez and Pascual Perez; also, Newsboy Brown and Jackie Brown.

14. Thru 1980, the only man born in Africa to win the flyweight championship was Victor (Young) Perez, who was born in Tunisia, in northern Africa.

15. Pascual Perez defended his title successfully ten times and boxed 21 nontitle bouts during that time. In nontitle bouts both boxers normally weigh in over the weight limit, but in 7 of his nontitle bouts both Perez and his opponent weighed in under the 112-pound limit, automatically placing the title at stake.

16. After winning his first professional bout, Englishman Jackie Brown lost 3 bouts within one month and then boxed a draw before turning his boxing career around and winning 17 of 19. Brown won 97 of 129 bouts in his pro career.

17. Just as Shoji Oguma has shown great perseverence (see question #2), so has his countryman Susumu Hanagata. Hanagata lost championship bouts to Efren Torres, Erbito Salavarria, Masao Ohba, and Chartchai Chionoi before knocking out Chionoi in a rematch to win the flyweight title.

18. In Fidel La Barba's third professional bout, in 1924, he met Jimmy McLarnin and lost a four-round decision. Two weeks later, in a rematch, they boxed a four-round draw. McLarnin started his career as a 15-year-old flyweight in 1923 and moved up through the ranks until he reached the welterweight class. He won and lost the welterweight title twice during the 1930s.

19. LaBarba, after winning the flyweight championship, outgrew the class and competed as a bantamweight and featherweight. Among his victories were wins over Bushy Graham, Bud Taylor, Tommy Paul, Petey Sarron, and Kid Chocolate, all of whom were champions. But LaBarba also lost to Bat Battalino and Kid Chocolate in two attempts at the featherweight title.

20. Before the discovery of penicillin, infections were not always easily cured. Filipino Pancho Villa died ten days after losing a nontitle bout with Jimmy McLarnin in 1925, from blood poisoning caused by an infected tooth.

21. There have been many champions who have won titles in more than one weight class and there have been many flyweights who have outgrown their class and moved up in weight. Yet only Masahiko (Fighting) Harada has won both flyweight and bantamweight championships. Harada also lost in two attempts at the featherweight title.

22. Scotsman Jackie Paterson was stopped ten times in his 91-bout career.

23. Pone Kingpetch lost his title to Masahiko (Fighting) Harada in 1962. Three months later, he won a rematch to become the first man to regain the flyweight title. He then lost to Hiroyuki Ebihara in his next bout and won the flyweight crown for the third time by capturing a rematch with Ebihara.

24. Prior to Kingpetch's feat, boxers had regained titles in all weight classes except flyweight. Kingpetch completed the cycle.

25. On November 20, 1971, Erbito Salavarria and Betulio Gonzalez met in Caracas, Venezuela, for the flyweight title. The bout was scored a draw. After the bout it was claimed that Salavarria illegally used sugar water between the rounds and the commission disqualified him.

ANSWERS The Flyweight Champions

26. On March 2, 1929, Emile (Spider) Pladner knocked out Frankie Genaro in 0:58 seconds of the first round—the quickest knockout in a flyweight championship bout. In the rematch, held on April 18, Genaro was awarded the bout on a foul in the fifth round.

27. On June 20, 1929, just two months after losing the flyweight title, Emile (Spider) Pladner met Eugene Huat for the French and European titles. In that bout, Pladner was knocked down 18 times before being stopped in the fifteenth round.

28. Mexican flyweight champion Miguel Canto received $160,000 for his defense against Ignacio Espinal of the Dominican Republic at Merida, Mexico, December 13, 1975. This was an all-time record purse for a flyweight. Espinal received $10,000 for his share.

29. When Rafael Lovera of Paraguay was signed to meet Luis Estaba of Venezuela for the WBC junior flyweight title, Lovera's record was given as 20-1-1 by the WBC. Estaba knocked Lovera out in the third round to win the title. Subsequently, it was disclosed that the bout had been Lovera's first professional bout.

30. After winning the title in his bout with Lovera, Luis (Lumumba) Estaba successfully defended his junior flyweight title ten consecutive times during 1976 and 1977 before being stopped by Freddy Castillo.

31. John Joseph (Rinty) Monaghan of Belfast, Ireland, was the flyweight champion from 1947 until his retirement in 1950. He is best remembered by boxing fans for his propensity for serenading the fans after his bouts—win, lose, or draw.

32. From February 3, 1940 until November 28, 1943, Valentin Angelmann competed in 43 bouts. Forty-two of these bouts went the distance of either 10 or 12 rounds. The other bout resulted in a knockout in the tenth round. Angelmann won 29, lost 10, and drew 4 of these contests. He won 121 of 176 bouts in his career.

33. Midget Wolgast was recognized by New York as the flyweight champion from 1930 to 1935. In 1935 he met Juan Zurita three times and defeated him all three times. Zurita moved up in weight and in 1944 became the NBA lightweight champion.

34. Jimmy Wilde holds this distinction. It is somewhat misleading since the Billy Papke whom he knocked out in 1911 was obviously not the same Billy Papke who was the middleweight champion, but rather another boxer who borrowed the name of the middleweight king. The

Jack Sharkey whom he met was a top-rated boxer sometimes known as "Little" Jack Sharkey and was not the man who later won the heavyweight title.

35. On June 18, 1923, Pancho Villa knocked out Jimmy Wilde in the seventh round at the Polo Grounds before 23,000 people. Villa won the world flyweight title in what was Wilde's last bout.

36. On September 30, 1949, Rinty Monaghan boxed a 15-round draw with Terry Allen of London to retain his World, British, British Empire, and European flyweight championships. This marked the first time that a boxer in any weight class defended four championships in one bout.

Other Champions

1. In 1943, Henry Armstrong lost only three bouts. Two of them were ten-round decisions to men named Walker who were or would become champions. Who were they?
2. There have been two champions who won both welterweight and middleweight titles, but were defeated in attempts for the light heavyweight title. Both had the same name. Who were they?
3. Who defeated Abe Attell, Tommy Loughran, Tony Galento, and five other champions?
4. What champion boxed 30 bouts in one year during the time he held the title, all of which went the scheduled distance to a decision?
5. Who boxed the most draws in championship bouts?
6. What champion had a winning streak of 62 consecutive bouts, lost 1 bout and then won 72 and drew 1 in his next 73?
7. Which champion defended his title twice within five days and five times within one month?
8. What champion defeated the largest number of other champions in both title and nontitle bouts?
9. Who was the champion who accepted a title defense in a situation in which he did not have the slightest chance of retaining his title?
10. What champions had the same name *(first* and *last)?*
11. Which champion was voted one of the ten greatest boxers of all time, but won fewer than half of his recorded bouts?
12. Two lightweight champions boxed the last bouts of their respective careers against each other. Who were they?

13. What champion lost the largest number of world championship bouts?

14. Who was the only champion to be named after a United States president?

15. Were there ever two champions at the same time who bore the same last name?

16. What lightweight champion won only 1 of 12 bouts after winning the championship?

17. Which lightweight champion beat a Baby, a Puppy, a Pee-Wee, a Babyface, an Angel, and a Lulu, but retired when he was knocked out by a Bunny?

18. What boxer competed for 22 years after his "retirement" from boxing?

19. Who was the only one of the eight boxers to take part in the Carnival of Champions in 1937 who never became a world champion?

20. When was the original Carnival of Champions?

21. In what bantamweight championship bout did both boxers compete barefooted?

22. Who were the only palindromic champions—fighters whose names were spelled the same backwards as forwards?

23. Who were the only men to enter the New York Golden Gloves and fail to win that tournament, yet later became professional world champions?

24. Which world champion was undefeated in his professional career but lost in his only appearance in the Eastern Regional Golden Gloves tournament to a man who would have greater success as an actor than as a professional boxer?

25. What champion closed out his career with seven consecutive draws?

OTHER CHAMPIONS

26. One middleweight champion lost 3 bouts in his first two years of boxing and then did not lose a single bout in his next 82 over 13 years. Can you name him?
27. What champion scored only 15 knockouts in his first 49 bouts and then scored 31 knockouts in his next 40 bouts?
28. Which champion won the most bouts on fouls?
29. What champion engaged in the most bouts ending by foul?
30. Which champion lost the most bouts on fouls?
31. What boxer lost 8 consecutive bouts and had 24 total losses before winning a championship?
32. Which champion lost the most bouts in his career?
33. Can you name the champion who defeated a bantamweight champion and also lost in a bid for the heavyweight title?
34. What champions competed as amateurs after their first professional bouts?
35. What championship bout holds the record for the most total knockdowns that were equally divided?
36. In which championship bout were the most total knockdowns recorded?
37. Which champion had only 10 knockouts in 86 bouts and then scored three knockouts in one month before he retired?
38. Who was the champion who lost four of his first five bouts and drew in the fifth bout?
39. What champion did not score a knockout in his last eight years of boxing, which included over 50 bouts?
40. Which champion only won one bout by decision in his career?
41. One champion survived a plane crash while champion. What is his name?

42. Which modern champion boxed six consecutive years without winning a decision?
43. What champion did not score a knockout in his first five years of boxing and then scored 30 knockouts in 41 bouts?
44. Who was the champion who was knocked out in his second professional bout and then was never stopped in the next 162?
45. What champion boxed five consecutive draws of 20 or 25 rounds?
46. Which champion won only 3 of his first 10 bouts and 7 of his first 17?
47. Who was the only champion whose last name was also his nationality?
48. What bout between the light heavyweight champion and a future heavyweight champion was called "no contest" when the referee disqualified both boxers for stalling?
49. Who was the only boxer to earn a college degree and win a world championship in the same year?
50. What champion was born on 12/12/12?
51. Has there ever been a champion who was a deaf mute?
52. Who held the welterweight championship for only three weeks?
53. What two champions faced each other fifteen times in championship bouts?
54. Which champion studied to be an architect and after retiring from the ring became an artist and had his work exhibited at the Pennsylvania Academy of Fine Arts?
55. What ex-champion played a role in the baseball "Black Sox" scandal?
56. Who is the only man to hold both World Boxing Association

OTHER CHAMPIONS [35]

and World Boxing Council titles in the same division at different times and lose each in his first title defense?

57. The Ali-Spinks rematch was part of a modern-day Carnival of Champions, with four championship bouts on the same card. The total purse for the eight boxers was $7,765,000. Juan Malvarez was one of the eight boxers in the four championship bouts. What percent of the total purse did he receive?

58. Who is the only man to win the New York Golden Gloves, Eastern Regional Golden Gloves, Intercity Golden Gloves, National AAU Championships, Olympic Games gold medal and a professional world championship?

59. There have been very few one-round knockouts in 12 seconds or less. Only one was scored by a man who later became a world champion. Who was he?

60. What champion had the lowest lifetime won-lost percentage?

61. What middleweight champion was married nine times?

62. Which welterweight champion lost his title because his opponent split his glove?

63. What champion in his first professional bout defeated a man he would later defeat for the championship?

64. Which champion died at the earliest age?

65. Who was the first man to win the same title three times?

66. In what championship bout did the two boxers have a combined total of 55 losses?

67. What lightweight was twice recruited from among the spectators to substitute for a boxer who was unable to appear?

ANSWERS

1. Armstrong lost on April 2, 1943, to Sidney Walker (Beau Jack), lightweight champion, in a nontitle bout. He lost to Walker Smith (Ray Robinson) future welterweight and middleweight champion on August 27, 1943.

2. Walker again. Mickey Walker won the welterweight title in 1922, middleweight title in 1926, and was defeated by Tommy Loughran in 1929 and Maxie Rosenbloom in 1933 in attempts at the light heavyweight crown. Ray Robinson (Walker Smith) won the welterweight title in 1946, added the middleweight belt in 1951, and lost to Joey Maxim in 1952 in an attempt to gain a third title.

3. Dr. Joyce Brothers, who had previously won $64,000 on the television show "The $64,000 Question," appeared on a spinoff of that show called "The $64,000 Challenge." She was challenged by eight former boxers who competed as a team and were defeated at the $64,000 level by Dr. Brothers.

4. Slapsie Maxie Rosenbloom, the light heavyweight champion, won 25, lost 3, and drew 2 bouts in 1932. Twenty-eight of these bouts went 10 rounds, 1 went 12, and 1 went 15 rounds. Only 1, against Lou Scozza, was a championship bout. Rosenbloom had 289 bouts in his career of which 262 went the distance. He won 187 of these, lost 33, and boxed 23 draws and 19 no-decision bouts.

5. There have been only 53 draws in championship bouts through 1980. Gene Fullmer had 2 in one year against Joey Giardello and Ray Robinson and three years later added a third as a challenger for Dick Tiger's title. But the all-time record is held by Abe Attell, featherweight champion from 1901 to 1912, who had 5 draws in that time in title bouts. He drew with George Dixon in 1901 for the vacant title, had another in 1905 against Kid Goodman, one in 1906 against Kid Herman, and 2 in 1908, both with Owen Moran—1 at 25 rounds and the other at 23 rounds. Attell had 17 draws in his career of 169 bouts.

6. Willie Pep won 62 bouts from the start of his career in 1940 until March 19, 1943, when he was defeated by Sammy Angott in a ten-round nontitle bout. Pep won the featherweight title from Chalky Wright in 1942 and did not lose another bout, after his defeat by Angott, until October 29, 1948, when he lost the title to Sandy Saddler.

ANSWERS Other Champions

He retired in 1959 and made a comeback six years later at the age of 43, winning 9 of 10 bouts before retiring permanently in 1966.

7. Henry Armstrong defended his welterweight championship five times within one month in October, 1939 including two defenses within five days on two occasions that month. He fought in five different cities and had bouts on October 9, 13, 20, 24, and 30. Tommy Freeman, welterweight champion in 1930-31, also defended twice within a five-day span and had five successful defenses within a two-month period.

8. Mickey Walker met 13 other champions throughout his career and had a 6-7-6 record with them. Sugar Ray Robinson met 18 other champions and defeated 13. But Henry Armstrong holds the record by defeating 15 champions of the 17 he faced. His record against these champions is:

2-0	Midget Wolgast	NYS flyweight champion
1-0	Benny Bass	World featherweight and junior lightweight champion
1-0	Petey Sarron	World featherweight champion
1-0	Leo Rodak	NBA featherweight champion
1-0	Chalky Wright	World featherweight champion
4-2	Baby Arizmendi	Mexico-California featherweight champion
3-0	Mike Belloise	NYS featherweight champion
1-1	Lou Ambers	World lightweight champion
2-0	Lew Jenkins	World lightweight champion
1-0	Sammy Angott	World lightweight champion
0-1	Beau Jack	NYS lightweight champion
2-0	Juan Zurita	NBA lightweight champion
1-0	Barney Ross	World lightweight, junior welterweight, and welterweight champion
1-0	Tippy Larkin	World junior welterweight champion
1-2	Fritzie Zivic	World welterweight champion
0-1	Ray Robinson	World welterweight and middleweight champion
1-0-1	Ceferino Garcia	World middleweight champion

Armstrong won 23, lost 7, and drew 1 and scored 11 knockouts while being stopped once (by Zivic). Only 8 of these bouts were title bouts.

9. Battling Siki, the light heavyweight champion, elected to meet

Mike McTigue in Dublin, reland, on St. Patrick's Day in 1923. The bout lasted the full 20 rounds, and, needless to say, the decision and the championship went to McTigue.

10. There have been a pair of Jack Dempseys, Joe Walcotts, and Young Corbetts who have been champions, but of these six men only one actually used his given name in the ring. Nonpareil Jack Dempsey was born John Kelly. Jack Dempsey, the heavyweight champion, was originally known as William Harrison Dempsey. Jersey Joe Walcott's real name is Arnold Raymond Cream, but the original Barbados Joe Walcott used his real name in the ring. Young Corbett II was actually William H. Rothwell and Young Corbett III was Ralph Capobianca Giordano.

There were two Tommy Kellys who were champions during the bareknuckle era and whose given names were both Tommy Kelly. Tommy "Spider" Kelly was bantamweight champion from 1887 to 1892 and Tommy Kelly of Boston was featherweight champion during the 1870s.

11. Benny Leonard, lightweight champion from 1917 to 1925, had 210 recorded bouts in his career yet only won 89 and drew 1. He boxed during the "no decision" era and had 115 bouts that went the distance and were recorded as no decision, due to state boxing laws in effect at that time.

12. It is very rare for two men to decide to retire from the ring after the same bout, but that is exactly what happened when Beau Jack and Ike Williams met on August 12, 1955. Jack was champion from 1942 to 1944 and Williams was champion from 1945 to 1951. They met three times prior to their final meeting, with Williams winning two and one ending in a draw. Williams stopped Jack in the ninth round of their final match in 1955, and both fighters retired afterward.

13. Emile Griffith had 26 championship bouts, of which he won 16 and lost 10, but one of those was for the American middleweight title and another was a 12-round bout billed for the WBA middleweight title at a time when Joey Giardello had nearly universal recognition as middleweight champion.

Tony Canzoneri engaged in 21 championship bouts of which he won 11, lost 9, and had 1 draw.

14. Jimmy Carter, the lightweight champion from 1951 to 1955 was named before the U.S. President. Carter, the boxer, was born on December 15, 1923, while Carter, the president, was born on October

ANSWERS Other Champions

1, 1924. But William Harrison Dempsey, who boxed as Jack Dempsey, was named after the ninth president of the United States, William H. Harrison.

15. There have been eight such sets of men: Panama Al and Jackie Brown, 1932 to 1935; Jose and Roberto Duran, 1976; Betulio and Rudolfo Gonzalez, 1972 to 1974, Tae-shik and Sane-hyun Kim, 1980; Chul-ho and Hwan-jin Kim, 1981; Archie and Davey Moore, 1959 to 1962; Eddie Mustafa and Matthew Saad Muhammad, 1980 to 1981; Solly and Mysterious Billy Smith, 1897 to 1898.

16. Wallace "Bud" Smith won 11 of his first 12 outings after beginning his career in 1948. He defeated Jimmy Carter for the lightweight championship in 1955 and successfully defended against Carter in a rematch. He then lost his next 11 bouts before retiring in 1958.

17. Lauro Salas, lightweight champion in 1952, met and defeated most of the top boxers in his division during his 16 year career. Included in his bouts were victories over PeeWee Swingler, Baby Leroy, Baby Face Gutierrez, Puppy Garcia, Angel Guerrero, and Lulu Perez. He announced his retirement after being knocked out in the tenth round by Bunny Grant in 1961.

18. Archie Moore retired in 1941, due to an extended illness, after a six-year boxing career. He decided to continue boxing one year later and competed for 22 more years, winning the light heavyweight championship in 1952 and holding it for 10 years, challenging twice unsuccessfully for the heavyweight championship.

19. Pedro Montanez, a Jewish Puerto Rican, holds that distinction. Montanez lost to Lou Ambers in 15 rounds in a lightweight title bout at the Polo Grounds in New York on September 23, 1937. Also on the same card were a bantamweight championship bout, a welterweight championship bout, and a middleweight championship bout. Harry Jeffra became the new bantamweight champ with a 15-round decision over Sixto Escobar. Barney Ross successfully defended his welterweight crown by outpointing Ceferino Garcia in 15 rounds. Garcia later won the New York middleweight title. The fourth bout was billed as a world title bout but recognition was refused by the New York State Athletic Commission. Fred Apostoli, the New York middleweight champion, knocked out Marcel Thil in the tenth round. Thil had previously gained recognition by the NBA as their middleweight champion. The paid attendance was only 32,600 with gross gate receipts of slightly more than $200,000. Jeffra only received $2,400 for his efforts while Ambers received $65,000. The others received amounts between those two extremes.

20. The original Carnival of Champions was a three-day event held at the Olympic Club, New Orleans, Louisiana, on September 5, 6, and 7, 1892. On the first day, Jack McAuliffe retained his lightweight championship with a 15-round knockout of Billy Myer. The next day George Dixon knocked out Jack Skelly in the eighth round to retain his featherweight crown. The final day saw the main event—a heavyweight championship bout between Jim Corbett and John L. Sullivan. This was won by Corbett by a knockout in the twenty-first round.

Ringside seats were priced at $25 for this bout, with a first-row seat priced at $100. Ringside tickets for the first day's action were $15, and $10 was charged for the second day's activities. As was the custom in those days, the boxers fought on a winner-take-all basis, and, in addition, put up their own side bets. The Corbett-Sullivan purse was $25,000 with an additional side bet of $10,000. Sullivan thus received nothing for his 21 rounds of boxing—losing his championship as well as $10,000.

21. On May 2, 1954, in Bangkok, Thailand, Jimmy Carruthers of Australia defended his title against Chamrern Songkitrat of Thailand in one of the most unusual championship bouts in modern history. The bout was scheduled for only 12 rounds, an oddity in itself, and was held outdoors despite a tropical rainstorm that started hours before the fight and increased in intensity as the bout progressed. Due to the extremely slippery conditions, both boxers requested, and received, permission to compete barefooted. Bulbs from the overhead lighting system crashed to the canvas every now and then and forced temporary halts while the ring was swept clear. Carruthers, however, stepped on glass in the eleventh round and cut his foot.

Mrs. Myra Carruthers and Mrs. Bill McConnell, wife of Carruthers' trainer, acted as seconds to Carruthers during this bizarre fight. This was the first world championship bout to be held in Thailand and thousands were turned away despite the storm. The bout was held in that weather since the Thai government had arranged half fares on all trains from all over the country and there were no accommodations to handle the throng that swarmed the city. There had been three consecutive days of heavy rain and there was no assurance that the rain would subside.

The bout was closely contested and after it was announced that Carruthers was awarded the decision, there was much booing.

ANSWERS Other Champions [41]

Songkitrat grabbed the ring microphone and calmed the crowd by saying, "I am very proud to have been able to bring fame to my country by being the first Thai boxer to contend for the world bantamweight title and I am personally satisfied that the decision was fair and beyond doubt. If I am not sorry, my friends and my countrymen, why are you?" Two weeks later, Carruthers retired as undefeated champion.

22. Willie Pep, featherweight champion from 1942 to 1950, and Lauro Salas, lightweight champion for five months in 1952, were the only champions whose last names read the same backwards and forwards. (Pep qualifies with an asterisk, as his given name is Guglielmo Papaleo.)

23. There have been 19 men who have become world champions who also competed in the New York Golden Gloves thru 1980. They include Ray Robinson, Gus Lesnevich, Emile Griffith, and Vito Antuofermo, all of whom were New York Golden Gloves champion. Lightweight champions Jimmy Carter and Paddy DeMarco, and light heavyweight champion Melio Bettina, as well as Saoul Paul Mamby, the junior welterweight champion, were the only New York Golden Glovers who won professional championships but failed to win the New York Golden Gloves. Carter lost his only bout in the 126-pound open class in 1943; DeMarco won three bouts in the 135-pound subnovice class before losing in the semifinals in 1945; Bettina lost in the 1934 175-pound open class finals and Mamby won five of eight bouts from 1965 to 1969 and reached the semifinals once.
[Note: This question started me on a 10-year research project that resulted in compiling the records of over 30,000 New York Golden Gloves bouts since 1927].

24. Rocco (Socko) Marchegiano competed for the Lowell, Massachusetts, team in the 1948 Eastern Regionals Golden Gloves competition against boxers from 12 other Eastern localities, including Pittsburgh, New York, Charlotte, North Carolina, and Puerto Rico. He was matched with Coley Wallace of New York in his first bout in a preliminary round held on the afternoon of March 1, 1948, at Ridgewood Grove and witnessed by only a handful of fans. The two boxers put on a war and Wallace was given a close decision. Shortly afterwards, Marchegiano turned professional and came to be known as Rocky Marciano. Wallace, a successful amateur boxer, was not very successful as a professional boxer. The highlight of his career was his portrayal of Joe Louis in the film The Joe Louis Story.

25. Bantamweight champion Jimmy Barry only boxed 9 draws in his 70-bout career. That number may seem high by today's standards, but Barry boxed at the turn of the century when draws were much more plentiful than they are now. He was the first champion to retire undefeated. He left the ring after boxing seven consecutive matches that were called a draw.

26. Carlos Monzon is in eighth place on the all-time list of longest consecutive undefeated streaks with 82 bouts in which he won 73 and drew 9. The only champions to surpass him on that list were Ray Robinson, Jimmy Wilde, and Ad Wolgast.

27. Middleweight champion Tony Zale had a record of 34-13-2 with only 15 knockouts from 1934 to 1939. He then turned his career around and won 36 of his next 40 bouts, including 31 by knockout.

28. Jack (Kid) Berg, the junior welterweight champion from England, won 14 bouts by foul during his 197-bout career. His career lasted from 1924 to 1945, but with all those fouls it's a wonder he lasted as long as he did.

29. Frenchman Andre Routis, featherweight champion in 1928-29, holds the record for total bouts ending in a claim of foul. He won 11 bouts by foul, second only to Berg, but he lost 6 bouts by foul, including two against Berg.

30. Mysterious Billy Smith, welterweight champion during the 1890s, lost 11 bouts due to his opponents claiming foul. He did not win a single bout on a foul—he was either a poor actor or an overaggressive fighter. He lost 4 of 10 bouts in 1900 on fouls including one with Rube Ferns for his welterweight title.

31. Fritzie Zivic lost 65 bouts in his career, far more than any other champion. From August 8, 1935, thru April 27, 1936, he lost 8 consecutive decisions and when he defeated Henry Armstrong for the welterweight title in 1940, he had a record of 98-24-5.

32. No other champion is close to Fritzie Zivic's record of 65 losses, 61 by decision. Lauro Salas is a distant second with 52 losses, and junior welterweight Johnny Jadick is third with 51.

33. Georges Carpentier began his career as an amateur flyweight in 1906 and boxed professionally from 1908 to 1927. He defeated Charles Ledoux in 1909. Ledoux won the bantamweight title three years later. Carpentier won the welterweight championship of Europe in 1911 and defeated Gunboat Smith in 1914 to claim the "white hope"

ANSWERS Other Champions [43]

heavyweight title. By defeating Battling Levinsky in 1920, he won the world's light heavyweight crown. In a bid for the world heavyweight championship, Carpentier was knocked out by Jack Dempsey in 1921 in a bout that attracted the first million-dollar gate.

34. Rocky Marciano, using the name Rocky Marsh, knocked out Lee Epperson on St. Patrick's Day in 1947. He then returned to the amateur ranks and won the Lowell, Massachusetts, Golden Gloves. He resumed professional boxing in July, 1948.

Henry Armstrong boxed professionally as Melody Jackson and had two bouts in 1931. He then tried out for the 1932 U.S. Olympic boxing team, but lost in the preliminary rounds of that tournament.

35. On December 10, 1958, light heavyweight champion Archie Moore defended his title against Canadian Yvon Durelle in Montreal. Even though Moore was knocked down three times in the first round, he came back and won the second round on points. Still in a daze, Moore boxed Durelle even for the next four rounds but was knocked down once more. In the seventh round, Moore knocked Durelle down for a count of three. By the tenth round Moore was in total command and had Durelle down for a second time before the bell saved him at the count of eight. In the next round Durelle took a nine count and finally a ten count as Moore evened the score at four knockdowns each at 0:49 of the eleventh round. This was Moore's one hundred and twenty-seventh knockout and the bout was acclaimed the "Fight of the Year" by The Ring.

36. Vic Toweel retained his bantamweight championship on December 2, 1950, by stopping Danny O'Sullivan in the tenth round in Johannesburg, South Africa. O'Sullivan was knocked down 14 times.

37. Bantamweight Lou Salica was never known as a powerful puncher, yet 6 of his total of 13 lifetime knockouts came in two spurts. He scored 3 knockouts in four bouts from May 15 to August 26, 1938, and then in 1944 he scored 3 knockouts in one month before losing a decision to Harry Jeffra and retiring.

38. Charley Phil Rosenberg started boxing in 1921. His record for that year was 0-4-1. In 1922, he only managed to win 5 of 8. He improved with an 8-6-2 record in 1923 and at the end of his first three years of boxing had a record of 13-13-3. By March of 1925 he was bantamweight champion. After losing his first bout in 1924, he won 10 and drew 1 and received a title shot in March 1925.

39. *Bantamweight Jimmy Walsh scored only 12 knockouts in 119 bouts in a 15-year career from 1901 to 1915. He scored his last knockout in 1908. He boxed in 50 bouts after that, and each went the distance. He won 9, lost 3, drew 11, and had 27 no decisions during that span.*

40. *Frankie Neil, bantamweight champion in 1903 to 1904, won a 25-round decision from Harry Tenny in 1905. (In a rematch in 1906, Tenny was knocked out in the 14th round and died shortly thereafter. This was the only decision that Neil won in his 56-bout career from 1900 to 1910. He won 24 by knockout, won 1 on a foul, lost 13, and had 17 draws and no-decision bouts.*

41. *Willie Pep was featherweight champion on January 8, 1947, when he was in a small airplane that overshot Newark Airport and landed in the woods in Middleville, New Jersey, killing five people. Pep had two broken vertabrae as well as a broken leg. He was in a cast until June, yet, incredibly, on June 17 he boxed and won a 10-round nontitle bout.*

42. *Mexican bantamweight Romeo Anaya won the world bantamweight title in January, 1973. He won a 10-round non-title bout by decision and then retained his title by winning a 15-round decision on April 28, 1973. He competed in 25 more bouts through 1980, with 9 bouts won by knockout, 11 bouts lost by knockout, and 5 bouts lost by decision. He boxed for 7 years without winning a decision.*

43. *Featherweight champion Clemente Sanchez compiled this strange record. His record through five years of boxing was 12-4-2 with all 18 bouts going the scheduled distance. He then won 27 of his next 31 bouts by knockouts, lost 3 by decision, and drew 1.*

44. *Joe (Sandy) Saddler was stopped in the third round of his second professional bout by Jock Leslie in 1944. Saddler had 160 bouts after that one and only lost 15 while scoring 103 knockouts himself and winning 143. He twice won the featherweight title and held the title from 1950 to 1957.*

45. *At the turn of the century bouts were often scheduled for 20 or 25 rounds. Draws were also more common during that era. Dave Sullivan, featherweight champion, boxed five consecutive bouts in 1899 that were scored as draws—three went 25 rounds and the other two went 20 rounds.*

46. *Billy Backus, welterweight champion from 1970 to 1971, had a*

ANSWERS Other Champions

very slow start in his professional boxing career. After his first 10 bouts, his record was 3-4-3, and after his first 17 bouts he only had a record of 7-7-3 from 1962 to 1965. He was inactive for 2½ years and then won 15 of 16 bouts on his way to winning the welterweight championship.

47. Freddy Welsh, whose real name was Frederick Hall Thomas, was a Welshman who won the lightweight championship in 1914 and held it until he was defeated by Benny Leonard in 1917.

48. Slapsie Maxie Rosenbloom, the light heavyweight champion, met James Braddock in a bout in Minneapolis on November 10, 1931, in a non-title bout. When neither boxer showed much aggressiveness, referee George Barton threw them both out of the ring and declared a "no contest" after 2 rounds.

49. Carlos Palomino won the world welterweight title in 1976 and also graduated from California State College at Long Beach in that year.

50. Henry Armstrong was born on December 12, 1912, in Columbus, Mississippi.

51. Bantamweight champion Mario D'Agata was a deaf mute. He won the world bantamweight title in 1956. Middleweight Eugene Hairston was another deaf mute who had a successful boxing career. He was a Golden Gloves champion but he never received a title shot. His professional ring record was 45-13-5 from 1947 to 1952.

52. After Mike (Twin) Sullivan abandoned the welterweight title in 1908, the championship changed hands quite frequently in the next seven years. On June 1, 1915, Mike Glover won a 12-round decision from Matt Wells for the title. On June 22, 1915, Glover was defeated by Jack Britton, also on a 12-round decision. Thus, Glover was welterweight champion for only 21 days.

53. One of the most famous series of boxing rematches was the duel between Jack Britton and Ted (Kid) Lewis. From 1915 to 1921 they faced each other 20 times in the ring. Britton won the series 4-3-1, with 12 no-decision bouts. Britton won the welterweight championship in 1915 and for the next six years the two took turns holding it. Fifteen of their matches were championship bouts.

54. Mickey Walker, welterweight and middleweight champion, originally studied to be an architect. Upon retiring from the ring, he continued his artistic endeavors and achieved a fair measure of success as a painter.

55. Bantamweight champion Abe Attell was one of the individuals who did the "leg work" for gambler Arnold Rothstein in attempting to fix the outcome of the 1919 World Series.

56. Light heavyweight Marvin Johnson, 1972 Olympic bronze medalist, won the WBC version of the light heavyweight title in December, 1978, and lost it in his first defense in April, 1979, to Matthew Franklin, who subsequently changed his name to Matthew Saad Muhammad. Undaunted, he challenged Victor Galindez in November of that year for Galindez's WBA title and won. In his first defense of that title in March, 1980, he lost to Eddie Gregory, who later became known as Eddie Mustafa Muhammad.

57. The gross gate receipts for this extravaganza were $4,806,675. Added to this was $5,100,000 for television rights. The total purses paid to the eight boxers was $7,765,000. Of this total, Muhammad Ali received $3,500,000 and Spinks received $3,750,000. Ali received 45% of the total purse and Spinks received 48%. The other three champions received the following amounts: $200,000 for Galindez and $100,000 each for Jorge Lujan and Danny Lopez. Challengers Mike Rossman and Alberto Davila each received $50,000 and poor Juan Malvarez was given only $15,000, or less than two tenths of 1% of the total purse.

58. Only 14 men have won both world championships and Olympic championships. Of these 14, only one, Floyd Patterson, also was a New York, Eastern Regionals, and Intercity Golden Gloves champion. In addition, Patterson also won the National AAU Championship.

59. Battling Nelson scored a knockout against Willie Rossler in only 12 seconds on April 5, 1902, in Harvey, Illinois.

60. Pinkey Mitchell, junior welterweight champion from 1922 to 1926, engaged in 79 bouts, but 50 of them resulted in no decision. Of the remaining 29 bouts, 4 were draws and 1 was called no contest. Only 24 of his 79 bouts resulted in a winner and Mitchell only won 12 of them for a .500 lifetime won-loss record. This is the lowest won-lost record of any champion.

61. Norman Selby, alias Kid McCoy, was middleweight champion from 1897 to 1898. He compiled a lifetime record of 81 wins, 6 losses, 9 draws, 9 no-decisions, and 9 wives.

62. Carmen Basilio defended his welterweight title against Johnny Saxton in Chicago in March, 1956. In the third round, Basilio knocked

ANSWERS Other Champions [47]

out Saxton, but the bell saved him. When Saxton came out for the fourth round he had a slit in his glove. The referee ordered that a new glove be put on. It took fifteen minutes to locate another glove, and by that time Saxton had fully recovered. Saxton lasted the 15 rounds and was awarded an unpopular decision. In two subsequent matches with Saxton, Basilio rewon the championship by a ninth round knockout and defended it successfully with a second round knockout.

63. Curtis Cokes defeated Manuel Gonzalez in a six-round bout in March, 1958, in Cokes's first professional bout and Gonzalez's seventh pro bout. They met four more times with Cokes winning three of the four. Their last meeting was in 1966 for the WBA welterweight title, which Cokes won.

64. Australian Les Darcy was recognized by some as the world middleweight champion from 1915 to 1917 although he never received universal recognition. He started boxing professionally at the age of 15 and died of an illness in Memphis, Tennessee, in 1917 at the age of 21.

65. Jimmy Carter won the lightweight title from Ike Williams in 1951. He lost that title to Lauro Salas in 1952 and rewon it later that same year. After three successful defenses, he lost it again to Paddy DeMarco in 1954. He rewon it again in 1954 and became the first man to win the same title three times.

66. When Freddie (Red) Cochrane met Fritzie Zivic for the welterweight championship on July 29, 1941, Zivic's record was 108-25-6. Cochrane had a record of only 63-30-9 but won the title from Zivic by a 15-round decision.

67. In 1911, Willie Ritchie was a spectator at a match between Freddie Welsh and Ad Wolgast when it was discovered that Wolgast would not be able to appear. Ritchie was recruited and boxed 20 rounds but lost the decision. Less than three months later he substituted for Packey McFarland and boxed a six-round no-decision bout with Young Erne.

Time Out

James J. Corbett was known as "Gentleman Jim," and held the heavyweight spotlight from the time he dethroned John L. Sullivan in 1892 through his defeat at the hands of Fitzsimmons some five years later and on through his comeback losses to James J. Jeffries. Later, Corbett became a combination sportswriter and ringside celebrity, something he handled better than his selections, since he consistently picked the wrong man to win in fight after fight. Before the Johnson-Jeffries fight, billed as "The Battle of the Century," Corbett allowed as how he thought Jeffries would win. "I'll bet you never picked a winner in your life," jeered a fellow writer. "Oh, yes, I did," shot back Corbett. "The time I fought Jeffries, I picked him to win after the first round."

When asked why he decided to retire from the fight racket, Rocky Graziano replied, "I looked in the mirror after my last fight and that beaten-up face looked back at me, and I decided right then and there that there must be an easier way to meet congenial people of my own age."

Philadelphia Jack O'Brien, one of the great light heavyweight boxers and light heavyweights talkers, once came up on the short end of things outside the ring. Seems O'Brien had gotten the representative from Nevada, who he had met through one of his customers in his gym, to introduce him to the-then President of the United States, Calvin Coolidge. As soon as Coolidge said, "How do you do?"—or something else as meaningful—O'Brien planned to make a full-fledged speech offering to teach the President the finer points of boxing without pain. However, when he got to the President's desk, O'Brien felt what he described in his flowery phrase as "such an aura of latent hostility that emanated from the fellow" that he choked up. He was almost immediately shoved out of the way to make room for a visiting troop of Boy Scouts before he was able even to begin his prepared speech.

Buddy Baer, the one-time heavyweight contender who took his fame and 6-foot 6-inch frame into show business, was once heckled by a man in the audience who called out, "Hey, Buddy, where'd you get all that gray hair?"

Baer retorted, "Did you ever fight Joe Louis twice?" And then, sighting his needler, he struck back with, "You've got plenty of gray there yourself."

"Yes," the heckler responded, "I bet on you both times."

John L. Sullivan, who liked to boast "I can lick any sonovabitch in the house," was downing a few beers one night in a Bowery saloon when a skinny little runt who had had a little too much of the bubbly staggered up to him and challenged him to a fight. The burly heavyweight champ picked up his would-be adversary by the scruff of the neck. Holding him three feet off the ground, he growled, "Listen, you! If you hit me just once—and I find out about it—you're in trouble."

That nattering nabob of boxing, Cassius Marcellus Clay, then a mere pretender to the heavyweight throne, once found himself on a promotion tour that included a strip tease joint just off Broadway. When one of the performers asked him how he felt about the big bout coming up, Clay pontificated, "I just pray that everything will come off all right." The so-called exotic dancers giggled and echoed his sentiments. "Me, too!"

While touring for the troops in World War II, Billy Conn and Joe Louis—who had been in what *The Ring* was later to call "The Greatest Fight of All Time" just the year before the War broke out—used to engage in on-stage badinage. One such dialogue had Conn, who had lost in the thirteenth round after having outpointed Louis handily in the first 12, saying to the Champ, "Joe, why didn't you let me win the fight?" intimating that they could have set up one helluva return bout. Louis, as eloquent outside the ring with his succinct statements as he was inside with his economical punches, merely said, "Billy, I gave you the title for 12 rounds, and you didn't know what to do with it. What would you have done with it for six months?"

Names

1. Which boxer has the most unpronounceable name?
2. In what middleweight bout during the 1950s did both contestants have rhyming names?
3. Who was the only boxer in history who was truthfully billed as "Greatest"?
4. Which professional boxer's surname began and ended with the letter X?
5. What championship bouts had these nick-names: "Thrilla in Manila" and "Rumble in the Jungle"?
6. What were the ring names of these champions?
    a. Rocco Barbella
    b. Noah Brusso
    c. Arnold Raymond Cream
    d. Louis D'Ambrosio
    e. Richard Ihetu
    f. Henry Jackson
    g. Leonard Liotta
    h. Guglielmo Papaleo
    i. Sidney Walker
    j. Archibald Lee Wright
7. During the 1970s there was a Canadian boxer named Horst Geisler who used a very unusual ring name. What was he known as?
8. There have been 15 champions through 1980 whose nickname was "Kid." How many can you name?
9. During the 1970s, four boxers named Lopez were popular—Alvaro, Danny, Eddie, and Ernie. What were their nicknames?

NAMES [51]

10. Which champion was known as "Poison"?
11. What champions bore these given names?
    a. Cecil
    b. Eligio
    c. Gerhardt
    d. Gershon
    e. Ignacius
    f. Janos
    g. Judah
    h. Lucien
    i. Oscar
    j. Ovila
    k. Ultimo
    l. Verlin
12. Who was the first boxer known as "Rocky" to achieve prominence?
13. What do all these boxers have in common: Attilio Castellani, Guy Casale, Rocco Barbella, Juan Rivero, and Gary Randall?
14. Through the years, boxing writers, fans, and others in the boxing world have given boxers some colorful nicknames. What boxers were known by these nicknames?

    These boxers were active in the early years of professional boxing with gloves:
    1900-1919
    a. The Boilermaker
    b. Gentleman Jim
    c. Terrible Terry
    d. Jack the Giant Killer
    e. The Durable Dane
    f. The Thunderbolt
    g. The Corkscrew Kid
    h. Ruby Robert

15. These men were the heros of the twenties and thirties: 1920-1939
    a. Slapsie Maxie
    b. The Toy Bulldog
    c. Homicide Hank
    d. The Cinderella Man
    e. The Orchid Man
    f. The Cuban Bon Bon
    g. Phaintin' Phil
    h. King of the Canebrakes
    i. The Jewel of the Ghetto
    j. The Fargo Express

16. These boxers were active during the early years of television: 1940-1959
    a. The Bronx Bull
    b. The Man of Steel
    c. Old Bones
    d. The Golden Boy
    e. The Mongoose
    f. The Brown Bomber
    g. The Will o' the Wisp
    h. The Hawk

17. Many of these men are still active in the ring today: 1960-1981
    a. Sugar Ray
    b. Smokin' Joe
    c. The Heat
    d. Gentleman Gerry
    e. Mister
    f. Mantequilla
    g. Guts
    h. The Hitman
    i. Bump City

18. Name the champion who defeated such boxers as Mighty Joe, Easy Dynamite, Black Power, Lion Ring, and Super Human Power.

NAMES

19. Under the Marquess of Queensberry rules (non-bareknuckles) there have been four heavyweight champions named James J. How many can you name?
20. Why is a boxer sometimes called a "pug"?
21. How many Jack Dempseys were there who were professional boxers?

ANSWERS

1. *Nkosana Mgxaji, a South African junior lightweight active in 1981 (with a record of 76-3-3 through 1980), is the undisputed champion in this category. Runners up for this title include Tongta Kiatvayupakdi, Thai junior welterweight; Tembisile Ngxingolo, South African flyweight; Sangthong Siththumrong, Thai Flyweight; Loyisa Myta, South African welterweight; Monde Mpulampula, South African flyweight; Petchsayarm Petcharern, Thai junior lightweight; and Veeranid Charemunuang, Thai featherweight.*
Mgxaji answers to the name of Happy Boy.

2. *William Butler, a middleweight from Bimini, in the Bahama Islands, boxed under the mellifluous name of Yama Bahama. On August 31, 1954, he was matched against a Chicagoan named Carlo Sarlo in a six-round bout in Detroit, which was won by Sarlo on a decision.*

3. *A Brooklyn middleweight who competed from 1958 until his death in the ring in 1966, and who compiled a record of 16-10-2, was the only boxer to be truthfully billed as Greatest. Although his ring ability was not the greatest, his given name was—Greatest Crawford.*

4. *Since* The Ring Record Book *was first published in 1941, more than 35,000 boxers' records have appeared. In that time, there have been only six men whose last names began with an X: Four South African boxers in the 1981* Ring Record Book, *Rolly Xipu, Gift Xaluwa, Vuyani Xabanisa, and Sazi Xhamlashe; Jose Xiala, a Cuban bantamweight who competed from 1956 to 1958 and compiled a 1-5-1 record; and Armand Xhonneux, a Belgian light heavyweight who compiled a 5-4-0 mark in 1974 to 1975. Xhonneux is also the only one whose name began and ended with an X.*

5. *Muhammad Ali took part in both of these historic bouts. The "Thrilla in Manila" was his third bout with Joe Frazier, held on October 1, 1975, and the "Rumble in the Jungle" was the October 30, 1974, bout in which he won the title from George Foreman in Kinshasa, Zaire.*

6.   **a.** *Rocky Graziano*
     b. *Tommy Burns*

ANSWERS Names

    c. Jersey Joe Walcott
    d. Lou Ambers
    e. Dick Tiger
    f. Henry Armstrong
    g. Tony DeMarco
    h. Willie Pep
    i. Beau Jack
    j. Archie Moore

7. The Canadian heavyweight Horst Geisler was billed as "Him." From 1973 to 1978 Him engaged in 14 bouts, all of which ended in knockouts. Him knocked out 8 opponents, including Chuck Wepner, and Him was knocked out 6 times Himself.

8. Champions named Kid were: middleweight Charles (Kid) McCoy; welterweights Kid Graves, Ted (Kid) Lewis, Kid Gavilan, Benny (Kid) Paret, and The Dixie Kid; junior welterweight Jack (Kid) Berg; lightweight George (Kid) Lavigne; junior lightweight Steve (Kid) Sullivan; junior lightweight and featherweight Kid Chocolate; featherweights Louis (Kid) Kaplan and Hogan (Kid) Bassey; junior featherweight Jack (Kid) Wolfe; and bantamweights Kid Murphy and Kid Williams. Surprisingly there have been no flyweight champions named Kid.

Nino Benvenuti, junior middleweight and middleweight champion, could also be added to this list as the name "Nino" in Italian translates freely as "Kid."

9. Alvaro (Yaqui) Lopez, Danny (Little Red) Lopez, Eddie (Animal) Lopez, and Danny's brother, Ernie (Indian Red) Lopez.

10. David (Poison) Kotey, WBC featherweight champion 1975 to 1976 from Ghana.

11. **a.** Cecil Lewis Thompson, known as Young Jack Thompson—welterweight champion
    b. Eligio Sardinias, known as Kid Chocolate—junior lightweight and featherweight champion
    c. Gerhardt Steffen, known as Willie Ritchie—lightweight champion
    d. Gershon Mendeloff, known as Ted (Kid) Lewis—welterweight champion
    e. Ignacius Pasquali Giuffi, known as Harry Jeffra—featherweight and bantamweight champion

f. *Janos Ruthaly, known as Jack Root—light heavyweight champion*
   g. *Judah Bergman, known as Jack (Kid) Berg—junior welterweight champion*
   h. *Lucien Brouillard, known as Lou Brouillard—middleweight and welterweight champion*
   i. *Oscar Battling Matthew Nelson, known as Battling Nelson—lightweight champion*
   j. *Ovila Chapdelaine, known as Jack Delaney—light heavyweight champion*
   k. *Ultimo Ramos Zaqueira, known as Sugar Ramos—featherweight champion*
   l. *Verlin Jenks, known as Lew Jenkins—lightweight champion*

12. Rocco Tozzo, although born in Buffalo, New York, was known as Rocky Kansas and was lightweight champion from 1925 to 1926. He was the first boxer known as Rocky to achieve a measure of success. He was also the only boxer known as Rocky during his career which spanned from 1911 to 1932. There have been more than 125 boxers since that were called Rocky.

13. Rocky Castellani, Rocky Casale, Rocky Graziano, Rocky Rivero, and Rocky Randall are among the more than 125 boxers to be called Rocky.

14.
   a. *Jim Jeffries*
   b. *Jim Corbett*
   c. *Terry McGovern*
   d. *Jack Dillon*
   e. *Battling Nelson*
   f. *Billy Papke*
   g. *Kid McCoy*
   h. *Bob Fitzsimmons*

15.
   a. *Maxie Rosenbloom*
   b. *Mickey Walker*
   c. *Henry Armstrong*
   d. *Jim Braddock*
   e. *Georges Carpentier*
   f. *Kid Chocolate*
   g. *Phil Scott*
   h. *Young Stribling*
   i. *Ruby Goldstein*
   j. *Billy Petrolle*

NAMES [57]

16.
   a. *Jake LaMotta*
   b. *Tony Zale*
   c. *Joe Brown*
   d. *Art Aragon*
   e. *Archie Moore*
   f. *Joe Louis*
   g. *Willie Pep*
   h. *Kid Gavilan*

17.
   a. *Ray Robinson, Ray Leonard, or Ray Seales*
   b. *Joe Frazier*
   c. *John Verderosa*
   d. *Gerry Cooney*
   e. *Reynaldo Snipes*
   f. *Jose Napoles*
   g. *Ishimatsu Suzuki*
   h. *Thomas Hearns*
   i. *Johnny Bumphus*

18. Dick Tiger, in his early career in Nigeria, met and defeated boxers using such ring names. Those names were definitely much easier to pronounce than some of the current African boxers such as Ncedo Mpetsheni, Obisia Nwakpa, Sazı Xhamlashe, and Mxolisi Mgidi.

19. James John Corbett, James Jackson Jeffries, and James Joseph Braddock were the easy ones—but did you know that Gene Tunney's given name was James Joseph?

20. The Latin word pugil, meaning one who fights with his fists, is the origin of the word pugilism, meaning boxing. A pug is a slang term for a boxer and comes from the same root.

21. John Kelly, who boxed as Jack Dempsey, "The Nonpareil," was born in Ireland and raised in New York. Another Jack Dempsey, a featherweight from Colorado in the 1890s, was really named Jack Dempsey, and defeated Young Corbett, among others. And then there was the second Jack Dempsey from Colorado, born William Harrison Dempsey, the heavyweight champion from 1919 to 1927.

Relatives

1. Twin brothers once boxed each other in Golden Gloves competition. Can you name them?
2. What New York Golden Glover married his opponent's sister two days before their championship bout?
3. Name the boxer who knocked out a father and his son in the same round 15 years apart.
4. What boxer was one of triplets?
5. Which heavyweight champion was the great-great-grandson of Charles Hunkerfoot, a full-blooded Cherokee Indian chief?
6. One heavyweight champion had a brother who won 20-games in one season in the major leagues. Who was he?
7. Who were the only brothers to challenge for the heavyweight championship?
8. Name the only brothers to challenge unsuccessfully for both the heavyweight and light heavyweight championships.
9. What do Abe Attell, Jim Braddock, Gene Fullmer, and Benny Leonard have in common?
10. Muhammad Ali's brother had a brief ring career. What was his given name and what name did he use in the ring?
11. What were the ring names of the Agati brothers Pasquale and James?
12. How many Elkins brothers were there who were professional boxers?
13. How identical were the ring careers of the twin brothers Jack (Twin) Sullivan and Mike (Twin) Sullivan? What weight classes did they compete in? How many bouts did they win?

How many bouts did they lose? In what years did they compete?

14. What father and son boxed on the same card in 1975?
15. The son of which heavyweight champion played a leading role in the "Beverly Hillbillies" television series?
16. Major league baseball player Dolph Camilli's brother was killed in the ring. Who delivered the fatal punch?
17. The father of what professional bowler held the record for scoring the quickest knockout?
18. What 1980s boxer nicknamed Boom-Boom is the son of a 1940s boxer also nicknamed Boom-Boom?
19. What three brothers all scored knockouts on the same card?
20. Middleweight champion Carmen Basilio is related to another champion. Who was he and what was the relationship?

ANSWERS

1. *The Outhouse twins, Gale and Gayus, were matched in a bout in the 1946 Sioux City Golden Gloves with Gale winning a decision. Both boxers later turned professional and had brief but successful careers.*

2. *In 1967 Long Tom Robinson met William Morris in the finals of the 175-pound subnovice class. Had they met earlier in the tournament it would not have been noteworthy. But two days prior to the bout, Robinson married Morris's sister. Robinson celebrated by defeating his new brother-in-law by decision for the championship.*

3. *Jersey Joe Walcott knocked out Phil Johnson in Philadelphia on June 22, 1936, in the third round. Johnson's son Harold was stopped for the first time in his career on February 8, 1950, by Walcott, also in the third round in Philadelphia.*

4. *The bareknuckle boxer William Thompson was one of triplets. He was more popularly known as Bendigo. This name was a twist on the biblical name Abednego, who was one of three brothers—the others being Shadrach and Meshach.*

5. *Joe Louis was able to trace his family tree back to his great-great-grandfather, who was a full-blooded Indian chief named Charles Hunkerfoot.*

6. *Jim Corbett's brother Joe, pitching for the Baltimore Orioles in 1897, had a 24-8 record.*

7. *Max and Buddy Baer were the only brothers to challenge for the heavyweight championship. Max was successful, defeating Primo Carnera for the title, but Buddy lost twice to Joe Louis in title attempts.*

8. *The Quarry brothers both challenged for those titles. Jerry Quarry lost to both Jimmy Ellis and Joe Frazier in heavyweight championship bids, and his brother Mike lost to Bob Foster for the light heavyweight title. Leon and Michael Spinks were both successful in their quest for those titles.*

9. *In addition to all being world champions, each of the four had two brothers who were professional boxers. Abe Attell's two brothers were Monte and Caesar. The Braddock brothers were Jimmy, Joe, and*

ANSWERS Relatives [61]

Al, Don, Gene, and Jay were the Fullmer brothers and the Leonards were Benny, Charley, and Joey.

10. Rudolph Valentino Clay is Cassius Marcellus Clay's brother. When Cassius became Muhammad Ali, Rudy became Rahaman Ali. Rahaman had a brief ring career but abandoned it to concentrate on furthering his brother's success.

11. The Italian Agati brothers used the Irish ring names of Packey O'Gatty and Jimmy O'Gatty.

12. There was only one Elkins Brothers. He was a heavyweight contender during the early 1950s. His lifetime record was 26-10-1 and included victories over Coley Wallace and Omelio Agramonte.

13. Although Jack and Mike Sullivan were twin brothers, their professional boxing careers were anything but identical. Jack was a middleweight from 1898 to 1922 and won 53, lost 18, and had 26 no-decision bouts and 41 draws. His brother Mike boxed from 1901 to 1914 as a lightweight and welterweight and won the welterweight title in 1907. He only had 69 recorded bouts and won 35, lost 7, and had 13 no-decisions and 14 draws. Mike died in 1937 and Jack died ten years later.

14. In Everett, Washington, on September 23, 1976, Rocky Mosley, Sr., was stopped in two rounds in his bout against Mike Lancaster. His son Rocky Mosley, Jr., avenged the defeat with a two-round knockout of his opponent Al Foster.

15. The part of Jethro Clampett was played by Max Baer, Jr. His father, Max Baer, Sr., and his uncle Buddy Baer were also actors after their boxing careers ended.

16. Frankie Campbell died after being knocked out by Max Baer in San Francisco on August 25, 1930. Campbell was the brother of Brooklyn Dodger first baseman Dolph Camilli.

17. Professional bowler Pete Couture is the son of ex-boxer Al Couture, who gained lasting fame by knocking out Ralph Walton in 10½ seconds in Lewiston, Maine, in 1946.

18. Ray (Boom-Boom) Mancini is the son of Lenny (Boom-Boom) Mancini, who was a top-rated welterweight and compiled a record of 42-12-3 from 1939 to 1947.

19. The Jiminez brothers—Chino, Fremio and Natalio—each scored a knockout on the same card on February 22, 1964, in Santo

Domingo, Dominican Republic. Fremio stopped his opponent in eight rounds, Natalio took four rounds while Chino needed only three rounds.

20. *Welterweight champion Billy Backus is the nephew of Carmen Basilio.*

The Boxing Hall of Fame

1. Where is the Boxing Hall of Fame?
2. Who were the first members elected to the Boxing Hall of Fame?
3. Who are the only heavyweight champions prior to Floyd Patterson who are not in the Hall of Fame?
4. Which Hall of Famer boxed the most draws?
5. Which Hall of Famer lost the most bouts by decision?
6. What Hall of Fame members have the same name?
7. What non-bareknuckle Hall of Fame member had the lowest knockout percentage?
8. One of the collections of the Boxing Hall of Fame consists of life-sized casts of famous boxers' fists. Who created these?
9. Who was the first non-bareknuckle boxer to be elected to the Hall of Fame who was *not* a world's champion?
10. What member of the Professional Football Hall of Fame is the grandson of a member of the Boxing Hall of Fame?
11. Who are the only brothers in the Boxing Hall of Fame?
12. Who are the only father-and-son members of the Boxing Hall of Fame?

ANSWERS

1. *The Boxing Hall of Fame is located in* The Ring *headquarters at 120 West 31st Street, New York, NY 10001. It is the only major sports hall of fame that does not charge admission.*

2. *There were 24 men elected to the Boxing Hall of Fame in 1954, in three groups: The Pioneer Group, the Oldtimers Group, and the Modern Group. They included James Figg, John Jackson, Daniel Mendoza, John Morrissey, Tom Hyer, Arthur Chambers, Jack McAuliffe, Tom Cribb, Jem Mace, John C. Heenan, Jack Broughton, Tom Sayers, Young Griffo, John L. Sullivan, and Jack (Nonpareil) Dempsey as members of the Pioneer Group; Stanley Ketchel, Jack Johnson, James J. Jeffries, Bob Fitzsimmons, Joe Gans, and James J. Corbett in the Oldtimers Group; and Jack Dempsey, Joe Louis, and Henry Armstrong in the Modern Group.*

3. *Floyd Patterson is the twentieth man to be heavyweight champion under the Queensberry rules. Only Marvin Hart, Primo Carnera, and Jim Braddock of these first 20 champions are not members of the Boxing Hall of Fame through 1980.*

4. *Both featherweights George Dixon and Young Griffo each boxed 37 draws including 3 with each other. Many bouts around the turn of the century were called draws by the referees to avoid further altercations among the spectators.*

5. *Fritzie Zivic lost the incredible number of 61 bouts by decision. Since his career included 230 bouts his won-lost record was still respectable at 155-65-10—a .705 won-lost percentage.*

6. *The Boxing Hall of Fame includes both Joe Walcotts (the original Barbados Joe and Jersey Joe) as well as the two Jack Dempseys (the Nonpareil and the Manassa Mauler).*

7. *Young Griffo only had 5 knockouts in 107 bouts for a .047 knockouts percentage, but he also boxed several bareknuckle bouts. Johnny Dundee had only 19 knockouts in 322 bouts for a percentage of .059, or one knockout in 17 bouts.*

8. *The collection of life-sized famous fists are the hobby of Dr. Walter H. Jacobs, a New York dentist who boxed as an amateur. The fists of Louis, Dempsey, Tunney, Armstrong, Johnson, and more than*

ANSWERS The Boxing Hall of Fame

80 others are a part of the collection, which also includes several bareknuckle boxers as well.

9. Sam Langford was elected in 1955. He boxed in 252 bouts from 1902 to 1924 and lost only 23. He boxed successfully in all classes from featherweight to heavyweight.

10. Art Donovan, Jr., was a defensive lineman for the Baltimore Colts during the 1950s. His father, Arthur Donovan, Sr., was a well-known boxing referee who refereed more heavyweight championship bouts than any other man and is a member of the Boxing Hall of Fame. His father, Professor Mike Donovan, was a bareknuckle middleweight champion and is also a member of the Boxing Hall of Fame.

11. The Gibbons brothers, Tommy and Mike, are the only brothers in the Boxing Hall of Fame. Tommy was a heavyweight who lost to Jack Dempsey for the title, and Mike was a top welterweight and middleweight boxer who only lost 2 of 114 bouts.

12. There are two sets of fathers and sons in the Boxing Hall of Fame: Art and Mike Donovan (see #10, above) and Jacob and Tom Hyer. Jacob Hyer was a bareknuckle boxer who claimed the championship in 1816. His son Tom was the first to achieve wide recognition as the American heavyweight champion in 1841. Both Hyers are members of the Boxing Hall of Fame.

The Olympic Games

1. One Olympic boxer had never boxed prior to his first Olympic bout and yet finished in third place. Who was he?
2. What Olympic boxing competition had the fewest countries entered?
3. What Olympian boxed only two bouts yet won two gold medals—both in the same year?
4. Have there ever been any other athletes to win two medals in boxing in one Olympic Games?
5. Who boxed the most Olympic bouts in one day?
6. When were the only Olympic Games since 1904 in which there was no boxing competition?
7. What Olympic boxer lost three bouts in one Olympic Games?
8. In which Olympic Games were there more bouts lost than won?
9. In which Olympic Games was a country not permitted to compete although a referee from that land worked some of the bouts?
10. Which country's only two Olympic boxing medals were won by a father and his son?
11. What individual has won the most Olympic boxing bouts by knockout?
12. What Olympian won a boxing gold medal at the age of 38?

THE OLYMPIC GAMES

13. How many Americans have boxed in two or more Olympic Games?

14. Who is the only Olympian to win boxing medals in two different Olympics as a representative of the United States?

15. Only one American has boxed the same opponent in two different Olympics. Who was he?

16. What individual won the most Olympic gold medals in boxing?

17. Who is the only Olympian to box in four Olympic Games?

18. Who lost the most Olympic bouts?

19. What two Olympic boxers competed for two different countries?

20. Name the Olympian who advanced to the final round while having had only one bout previously while his opponent in that final bout had had four previous bouts in the tournament.

21. What country has never won a boxing match in the Olympic Games but has produced more than ten boxers who have become world champions as professional boxers?

22. How many ex-Olympians has Muhammad Ali defeated as a professional boxer?

23. In which Olympic Games since 1904 was the featherweight boxing championship contested between two representatives of the United States?

24. In both the 1948 and 1952 Olympic Games the bantamweight class had two boxers who did not last beyond the quarter-final round, but would later win world's championships. Who were these four men?

25. When was the last Olympic Games prior to 1980 in which the United States Olympic boxing team failed to win at least one bout?

26. When was the last Olympic Games prior to 1980 in which the United States Olympic boxing team failed to win at least one gold medal?

27. Which Olympic champion and heavyweight championship contestant patented an improved trapshooting method?

28. Who were the only two men to compete against each other in the New York—Chicago Intercity Golden Gloves and also in the Olympic Games?

29. What Olympic champion won a purse of $2 million in his third professional bout?

30. Who is the only man to win both an Olympic bronze medal and a world heavyweight championship?

31. What future world's champion lost in the finals of the Olympic Games but was not awarded a silver medal?

32. Which professional boxing champion was knocked out in his only Olympic bout?

33. What Olympic champion boxed professionally for 29 years but never challenged for the world's title?

34. What future world's champions boxed each other in Olympic bouts?

35. What is the last name of a boxer named Sugar Ray who won the gold medal in the 139-pound class in the 1972 Olympic Games?

36. What Olympic bronze medal bore the name of a world light heavyweight champion?

37. Who was the only Olympian to finish fourth and later win a world championship?

38. What Olympian boxed for the world heavyweight championship in his first professional bout?

39. What Olympic champion lost the most bouts as a professional?

THE OLYMPIC GAMES

40. Who was the first Olympic champion to win a world's professional championship?

41. Who was the first Olympian to win a world professional championship?

42. What Olympic wrestler won a world boxing championship?

43. Who is the only man to be knocked out in the Olympics and later win the world's heavyweight championship?

ANSWERS

1. Fred Gilmore of Chicago, whose father, Harry, was a successful professional boxer, decided to enter the 1904 Olympic competition even though he had never before boxed in competition. He lost his first bout but since there were only two other contestants in his class (125 pounds) he finished in third place.

2. The 1904 Olympic Games in St. Louis had only 28 entrants—all from the United States.

3. Oliver L. Kirk of St. Louis won both the 115-pound and 125-pound classes on the same day in 1904. He only needed to box two bouts since there was only one other contestant in each of those classes.

4. Doubling up was common in 1904, and five boxers competed in more than one class. Oliver L. Kirk won two gold medals in two bouts. George V. Finnegan won at 105 pounds and lost to Kirk in the 115-pound class. George V. also won two medals in only two bouts but one was silver. Charles Mayer of New York won the 158-pound class but lost the heavyweight final bout in which he was outweighed by 24 pounds. His two medals were also gained in only two bouts. Harry J. Spanger of Newark, N.J., was the fourth man that year to win two medals. However, he was required to box five bouts in two days in winning the 135-pound title and losing in the finals of the 145-pound class. A fifth boxer also competed in two classes, Joseph Lydon of St. Louis. He lost his first bout in both the 135-pound and 145-pound classes.

5. In the 1908 Olympic Games the boxing competition was held in only one day. In the lightweight class 12 men were entered. Frederick Spiller of Great Britain won three bouts before losing his fourth bout of the day in the finals to Frederick Grace, also of Great Britain. Grace had drawn a bye in the semifinals and was only in his third bout of the day. There were only 42 competitors from four nations (32 from Great Britain) who took part in the boxing competition in the 1908 Olympic Games in London.

6. Although there was Olympic competition in fencing, wrestling, and shooting in Stockholm in 1912, there was no boxing since it was prohibited by Swedish law at that time.

ANSWERS The Olympic Games

7. Peter Sturholdt in the 1904 Olympics lost his first-round bout in the 135-pound class, but after the bout it was discovered that his opponent had used an alias. He was disqualified and Sturholdt was allowed to remain in the tournament. Sturholdt lost his next bout that day in the semifinal round. On the following day the semifinal losers were matched for third place and Sturholdt made his record 0-3 for the 1904 Olympic Games by losing his third match in two days.

8. In 1976 in Montreal, due to the withdrawal of many of the African nations after the draw had been prepared, bouts were scheduled in which neither contestant appeared. These were officially recorded as no-contest and recorded as a loss for both contestants. There were 6 such bouts. There were also 72 other bouts in which only one boxer appeared and was awarded the decision by default or "walkover."

9. In the Montreal Olympic Games in 1976, the Republic of China (Taiwan) was not recognized by the Canadian government and was prohibited from competing. However, a referee from Taiwan, Tung-Yong Hong, remained in Montreal and refereed.

10. The Philippines competed in every Olympic boxing competition from 1932 through 1976. In 1932, Jose Villanueva won the bantamweight bronze medal. His son, Anthony, won the silver medal in the featherweight class 32 years later. There have been 36 other Olympic boxing contestants from the Philippines, none of whom have won a medal.

11. Teofilo Stevenson of Cuba, the only three-time Olympic heavyweight champion, won his first three bouts in 1972 by knockout. He won his final bout by default when Ion Alexe of Rumania was unable to compete due to an injury suffered in an earlier bout. Stevenson won all four of his bouts in 1976 by knockout and became the first Olympian to win seven bouts by knockout and the first two-time heavyweight champion. In 1980 he extended his record by winning his first two bouts by knockout and then winning two decisions to claim his third Olympic heavyweight championship. His record from 1972 to 1980 is 12 bouts, 12 wins, 9 knockouts, 2 decisions, 1 default, and 3 gold medals.

12. Richard K. Gunn, representing the Surrey Commercial Docks B. C. and the Gainsford A. C. of Great Britain, won three bouts in one day in London, 1908, to win the featherweight title at the age of 38.

13. The United States has had only three boxers who competed in more than one Olympic Games—Davey Armstrong in 1972 at 106 pounds and 1976 at 125 pounds; Edward Eagan, light heavyweight in 1920 and heavyweight in 1924, and Ronnie Harris, lightweight in 1964 and 1968.

14. Of the three Americans who boxed in more than one Olympic Games, only Ronnie Harris won medals in two different years. He won the bronze medal in 1964 and the gold in 1968. Edward Eagan won the gold medal in 1920 as a light heavyweight boxer and won a second gold medal as a member of the United States bobsled team at Lake Placid in 1932. He is the only man to win medals in both summer and winter Olympic Games.

15. Rematches in Olympic boxing are quite rare. Ronnie Harris is the only American to engage in one. He avenged his 1964 semifinal loss to Josef Grudzien of Poland by winning a unanimous decision over Grudzien for the gold medal in Mexico City in 1968.

16. Laszlo Papp of Hungary was the only man to win three gold medals in Olympic boxing until 1980 when Teofilo Stevenson matched his accomplishment. Papp won the middleweight (160 pound) title in 1948 by winning 5 bouts with three knockouts. In 1952 the weight limits were changed and two additional weight classes were added. Papp entered the light middleweight (156 pound) class and again won 5 bouts with two knockouts including one over Ellsworth "Spider" Webb of the United States. Papp again won the light middleweight class in 1956 although he only had one knockout in 3 bouts. He won the championship with a decision over Jose Torres of the United States. Torres later became world light heavyweight champion. Papp turned professional at the age of 31 and was undefeated in 29 bouts. He was European middleweight champion from 1962 to 1965 when he was ordered to retire by the Hungarian government.

17. There have been a few boxers who competed in three different Olympic tournaments, but until 1980 no one had competed in four different Olympic Games as a boxer. In that year, Hungarian Gyorgy Gedo became the first man to do so by competing in the 106-pound class for the fourth consecutive Olympiad. He lost his first bout in 1968, won the championship in 1972, and lost in the quarter-final round in both 1976 and 1980. His total Olympic won-lost record stands at 8-3.

18. Only one man has competed in boxing in four Olympiads, yet two men have managed to lose four Olympic bouts. Until 1948, the semifinal losers would compete in a bout with the winner receiving the

ANSWERS The Olympic Games

bronze medal. Since 1952, both semifinal losers are awarded bronze medals. Flyweight Frantisek Majdloch of Czechoslovakia lost a semifinal bout in 1948 and lost again in the bout for third place. He competed again in 1952 and 1956 but lost in preliminary rounds in both years. Sverre Sorsdal of Norway competed from 1920 to 1928 as a light heavyweight and heavyweight. He won the silver medal in 1920, the bronze medal in 1924, and finished fourth in 1928. He, too, was a semifinal loser as well as a loser in the bout for third place in 1928. For his three Olympic appearances he had a record of 7-4 and two medals. Gyorgy Gedo, the only man to compete in four Olympiads, won the gold medal in 1972 and has a lifetime Olympic record of 8-3.

19. In 1964, East and West Germany competed as one team called Germany. Jurgen Schlegel, a light heavyweight boxer, was a member of that team. In 1968, separate teams were sent by the German Democratic Republic and the Federal Republic of Germany. Schlegel was a member of the German Democratic Republic team in that year. He showed no political favoritism as he won one and lost one in each of his two Olympiads.

In 1958, Egypt and Syria united to form the United Arab Republic. Although the political union was disbanded in 1961, Egypt retained the name of UAR until 1971. Abdelha Khallaf Allah competed for them in 1968 representing the UAR and in 1972 representing Egypt.

20. Michael Spinks of the United States received a bye in the first round of the middleweight class in Montreal in 1976. Rufat Riskiev of the USSR knocked out his Finnish opponent in his first-round bout. Spinks was scheduled to meet a boxer from the Cameroon in the second, but his opponent did not appear and Spinks received a victory by default. Riskiev meanwhile defeated his Bulgarian opponent by a decision. In the quarter-final round Spinks finally had to box and he defeated his Polish opponent by a unanimous decision. Riskiev knocked out his Pakistani foe in his quarter-final bout. In the semifinals Spinks was matched with a Rumanian, but the Rumanian was forced to withdraw, due to an injury suffered in a previous bout. Riskiev defeated his Cuban opponent by a 3-2 margin in a close bout. Thus Spinks arrived at the final round having had only one actual bout while Riskiev had had four bouts. Spinks won the gold medal by knocking out Riskiev in the third round.

21. The Republic of Panama has entered the boxing competition in the Olympic Games only twice through 1980. In 1964, Alfonso Frazer entered at 125 pounds and lost his only bout. In 1972, their two-man boxing team consisted of bantamweight Luis Avila and lightweight Roy Hurdley. Both of these boxers also lost their only bouts. Nevertheless, Panama has produced many world-class professional boxers, including world champions Roberto Duran, Jorge Lujan, Eusebio Pedroza, Ismael Laguna, and Panama Al Brown.

22. Six. In addition to his victories over Olympic Champions Floyd Patterson, Joe Frazier, George Foreman, and Leon Spinks, Ali also defeated Henry Cooper, who lost his only Olympic bout in 1952, and Rudi Lubbers, who represented The Netherlands in both the 1964 and 1968 Olympic Games. No other heavyweight champion has defeated as many ex-Olympians.

23. In 1920 and 1924, each country was permitted two contestants in each weight division in the Olympic boxing competition. In 1924, both Americans reached the finals of the featherweight class. Jackie Fields, who later became world champion, defeated Joe Salas for the gold medal. During that era there were two other exclusive Olympic boxing finals. The middleweight gold medal in 1924 was contested for by two Englishmen and the featherweight division in 1920 was decided between two Frenchmen.

24. Both Jimmy Carruthers of Australia and Vic Toweel of South Africa lost in the 1948 Olympic Games. Toweel lost his first bout to the Argentinian Arnoldo Pares. Carruthers defeated Pares in the second round of competition, but was defeated in the quarter-finals by the eventual gold medalist, Tibor Csik of Hungary. Toweel won the world bantamweight title in 1950 and lost it to Carruthers in 1952. In that year in Helsinki, Raul Macias of Mexico and David Moore of the United States both lost in their bids for an Olympic medal. Four years later, Macias was the NBA bantamweight champion. In 1956, Brazilian Eder Jofre, another future champion, lost in the quarter-final at the Melbourne Olympic Games. Moore won the world featherweight title and Jofre won the world bantamweight title in 1960.

25. The last Olympic Games prior to 1980 in which the United States did not win a single bout was in 1912 in Stockholm. The reason was that there was no Olympic boxing that year. In the previous Olympics, in London in 1908, boxing competition was held, but the United States did not enter.

26. In London in 1948, Horace Herring won a silver medal in the 147-pound class for the only American medal in boxing that year. Also

ANSWERS The Olympic Games [75]

on that team were Chuck Spieser and Wallace (Bud) Smith, both of whom later became successful professional boxers.

27. Pete Rademacher, 1956 Olympic heavyweight champion, boxed professionally for six years and compiled a 15-7-1 record. His interest in trapshooting led him to patent a trapshooting training device and develop a method called "instinct shooting," which he later taught to President Dwight D. Eisenhower.

28. Tony Madigan of Australia competed in the 1952 Olympic Games and lost in the quarter-final round of the 165-pound class. Madigan again lost in the quarter-finals in the 1956 Olympic Games. In 1959 he came to the United States and entered and won the New York Golden Gloves and Eastern Regional Golden Gloves tournaments. He represented the New York team in the intercity competition against Chicago and lost a decision to Cassius Marcellus Clay in the 175-pound class. In 1960 in Rome, Clay represented the United States in the Olympic Games and Madigan represented Australia. Both won their first two bouts and met in the semifinals with Clay winning a unanimous decision. Clay went on to win the gold medal, while Madigan received a bronze medal as a semifinal loser.

29. Patrizio Oliva of Italy, the only 1980 Olympic boxing gold medalist from a non-Communist nation, made his professional debut later that year. In his third bout, he defeated Brazilian Benedict Dos Santos and received a purse of two million lire (about $2,500).

30. Big John Tate won his first two bouts by decision in the 1976 Olympic Games, including a decision over Peter Hussing, the 1972 bronze medalist. Tate then had the misfortune to be matched against Teofilo Stevenson in the semifinal bout. He became Stevenson's sixth knockout victim in 1:29 of the first round, but as a semifinal loser was awarded the bronze medal. Three years later he won the WBA heavyweight championship.

31. Ingemar Johansson suffered the ignominy of being disqualified in the second round for allegedly "not trying" in the final bout of the 1952 Olympic heavyweight class against Ed Sanders of the United States. Since he was disqualified, he was not permitted to receive the silver medal, which he had earned by virtue of his four victories earlier in the tournament. Johansson, who could never be accused of "not trying" as a professional, won the heavyweight championship in 1959 and compiled a lifetime record of 26-2.

32. Italy's Bruno Arcari was knocked out in the second round of the 1964 lightweight class by Alex Oundo of Kenya. Oundo was ousted in his next bout by Josef Grudzien of Poland who went on to win the gold medal. Arcari was knocked out in his first professional bout later that year, but won the junior welterweight title in 1970.

33. Lambertus (Bep) Van Klavern of the Netherlands won the featherweight championship in the 1928 Olympic Games held in Amsterdam. Later that year he became a professional boxer and campaigned successfully through 1956. He won the European Boxing Union lightweight and middleweight championships during the 1930s, but never received the opportunity to box for the world title. He competed in the United States from 1932 to 1936 and defeated Ceferino Garcia, among others. His lifetime record was 78-21-8.

34. Through 1980 there have been three Olympic bouts in which both participants later became world champions. In 1908 in London, Matt Wells of Great Britain decisioned Waldemar Holberg of Denmark in a lightweight bout. They never met as professional boxers, although both were welterweight champions in 1914. In the very first flyweight bout in 1932 to 1937 Lou Salica defeated Canadian Jackie Callura. In 1940, they met in a ten-round nontitle bout that ended in a draw. Salica won the bantamweight championship twice during his career, while Callura was NBA featherweight champion briefly in 1943.

The third Olympic match between two future champions was the welterweight bout between Giovanni "Nino" Benvenuti and Ki-Soo Kim in Rome in 1960. Benvenuti won a unanimous decision in his homeland and went on to capture the gold medal. He won the WBA junior middleweight title in 1965 but made the mistake of defending it against Kim in Seoul, Korea, the following year. Kim won a 15-round decision in his native land and became junior middleweight champion. Benvenuti moved up to the middleweight class and won that title in 1967.

35. The forgotten Sugar Ray's last name is Seales. He was the United States boxing star in Munich on a team that included Marvin Johnson and Duane Bobick. The world watched as one by one the American boxers were eliminated and only Seales managed to reach the finals and win a gold medal.

36. A welterweight from Kenya in 1972 was called Dick Tiger Murunga. His hero, obviously, was the Nigerian middleweight and light heavyweight champion Dick Tiger, who, unfortunately, did not live to see his namesake win the bronze medal in the Olympics.

ANSWERS The Olympic Games

37. Since 1952 both semifinal losers have shared third place and two bronze medals have been awarded. In prior years the two semifinal losers had to compete in an extra bout to determine third and fourth place and only one bronze medal was awarded to the third place winner. From 1920 to 1948 there were 48 men who finished in fourth with two losses in the tournament. Only one man later won a world's championship—Wallace "Bud" Smith, the American lightweight who finished fourth in 1948. He was the world lightweight champion in 1955 to 1956.

38. In what was more of a publicity stunt than anything else, 1956 Olympic heavyweight champion Peter Rademacher challenged world heavyweight champion and 1952 Olympic middleweight champion Floyd Patterson on August 22, 1957. This was the first heavyweight championship bout in which odds were not given, yet Rademacher surprised everyone by scoring a knockdown and lasting six rounds before being knocked out. Although Rademacher had no place to go but down after that title bout, he campaigned for six years and compiled a respectable record of 15-7-1.

39. Frankie Genaro compiled a record of 83-22-9 with 15 no-decisions in 15 years of professional boxing. As most other Olympic champions did not box nearly as many bouts as professionals, Genaro's total of 22 losses is more than any other Olympic champion. Genaro is but one of only 14 men (through 1980) to win an Olympic gold medal and a world championship.

40. Although Frankie Genaro won an Olympic championship in 1920 and the American flyweight title in 1923, he did not win the world championship until 1928. Fidel La Barba meanwhile won the 1924 Olympic flyweight championship and the world flyweight title in 1929. Jackie Fields also was an early Olympic and world champion, but he won his titles in 1924 and 1929.

41. Both Waldemar Holberg and Matt Wells boxed in the 1908 Olympic Games in the welterweight class. Both men also won a claim to the world welterweight championship in 1914, but Holberg was first. He won a bout on New Year's day and held his claim for 24 days. Wells won the title in March, 1914, and retained his claim until June, 1915.

42. Paul Berlenbach was a wrestler on the United States Olympic team in 1920 and was the 1920 national AAU light heavyweight wrestling champion as well. (He was not Olympic champion, as has been *incorrectly stated in some books.) He became a professional boxer in 1923 and two years later won the light heavyweight championship of the world. He tried professional wrestling briefly in 1929 and then returned to boxing before retiring from the ring.*

43. *Big John Tate was knocked out by Teofilo Stevenson of Cuba in the 1976 Olympic semifinal round and was awarded a bronze medal. In 1979, he won the WBA heavyweight championship.*

Time Out

When Joe Louis visted the offices of Life Magazine, back in the days when both were champs of their respective divisions, he faced a long line of office boys and employees, all seeking his autograph. "Jus' wait," said Louis to one of the editors in his soft-spoken manner, "I'll bet they'll have bad pictures for me to sign."

"What do you consider a good picture of yourself?" asked the editor, who was conducting Louis through the maze of offices.

"Why, I like 'em when I'm standing up," replied the champ.

Willie Pep was known as "The Will O' The Wisp," and fighting him, to quote one of his many frustrated opponents, was "like trying to stamp out a grass fire."

One time Willie met a pretty good puncher out of Austin, Minnesota, named Jackie Graves, who had won twenty fights by knockout and lost only two in thirty-nine fights. Before the fight, Willie told a newspaper columnist with the local Minneapolis paper that he was not going to throw a punch in the third round. "So," according to Willie, "I moved around, feinted, picked off his punches, made him miss, and never threw a punch." And what happened? All three officials gave Pep the round.

Touching Moments in Boxing History Department: Hustling promoter-match-maker Don Elbaum set up Sugar Ray Robinson's last fight in 1964. After the Sugarman lost a 10-round decision to Joey Archer in Pittsburgh, there was a testimonial dinner for the great one. Robinson, not Elbaum.

In honor of his retirement, people presented various gifts to Ray. Elbaum found himself "Tapioca," but still he had to come up with a gift.

That 110-watt bulb in his head lit up. Elbaum stood up and silenced the gathering.

"Ray, don't ask me how I did it," he said seriously. "Don't ask me about the trouble and expense I went to. But I've got a special gift. I've got the gloves you wore in your first professional fight."

The house lights went down and Elbaum ducked out a side door. He reached into the trunk of his car, grabbed two gloves and ran back inside. Up go the lights as Robinson and his wife, touched by the

[79]

present, dissolve into tears.

As he handed the gloves to Ray, Elbaum noticed his mistake—both gloves were left-handed.

The New York State Athletic Commission was once chaired by a former lingerie salesman named John J. Phelan, whose working knowledge of the busted beak profession was just passing. Once when General Phelan (he was a major-general in the New York National Guard) was asked to sanction an exhibition bout involving Joe Louis, then heavyweight champion, he turned down the request on the basis that because there was no weight limit among heavyweights, Louis's title would be on the line, even in an exhibition bout. When it was pointed out that other heavyweight champions had engaged in exhibition bouts in Buffalo, that city of almost a million inhabitants in upstate New York, the General proved that his knowledge of geography just about matched his knowledge of boxing. "I don't care what they do in those foreign states," he said adamantly.

Newspapermen like to tell aobut the time a sports editor in the mold of Bugs Baer, former writer for the late New York American, was hard at work concocting his daily column when a fight manager came in with his charge, trying to sell a column.

Without waiting for a how-do-you-do, the fight manager started right in: "Meet the heavyweight champion of South Africa," he said, blowing himself up to pouter-pigeon proud.

"Who let you in?" the sports editor wanted to know. "Sorry, can't talk to you now. I'm busy. Some other time, maybe."

But the manager was persistent and continued to tug at the sportswriter's mental locks. "But you've got to meet him . . . Really, this is the newly-arrived champion from South Africa, and he would make a good story."

Still, the sports editor wanted no part of the manager or his fighter and waved them both away with a "Sorry, too busy."

Once again the manager tried selling his wares. "Come on now, you oughta meet this kid . . . He's the champion of South Africa . . .

But even before the last syllable of the word Africa had come out of the mouth of the manager, the sportswriter, now highly annoyed because his work had been disturbed, looked up for the first time, rose from his seat and brought up as beautiful a wallop as had ever been seen, in or out of the ring. It landed with a resounding thwack on the jaw of the fighter standing over him, and soon the fighter standing over him was reclining on the floor under him. "Now I'm the champion of South Africa," the writer muttered, sitting back down at his typewriter and going on with his work.

The champions trained by Ray Arcel through the years could make up a veritable Hall of Fame: Benny Leonard, Barney Ross, Tony Zale, Ezzard Charles, Jackie "Kid" Berg, Freddie Steele, Ceferino Garcia, Lou Broulliard, Jackie Fields, Sixto Escobar, Jim Braddock, and Roberto Duran, to name a few. The famous trainer also trained twelve fighters who were victims of Joe Louis. In fact, Arcel was dubbed "the Meat Wagon" by sports cartoonist Willard Mullin, because of his having to drag so many of his charges back to the corner after Louis had dispatched them.

It got so that, according to Arcel, "I'd get into the ring with my fighter and Louis would say, 'Man, you here again?'"

Harry Jeffra, former bantamweight and featherweight champ, is the only fighter in boxing history who took two days to win a title. Fighting as part of the Carnival of Champions in the Polo Grounds in 1937, Jeffra went on last, after Barney Ross, Lou Ambers, and Marcel Thil had defended their championships in an effort to wrest the bantamweight title from Sixto Escobar. Sitting in the dressing room awaiting his turn in the ring, Jeffra remembers that his manager "bought a pillow and blanket to the stadium so that I could get some sleep. But I kept waking up . . . and I didn't like what I was seeing. First, Thil comes in, and he's a real mess after [Fred] Apostoli knocked him out. Then, a little later, they drag in [Ceferino] Garcia. And his face looks like chopped meat after Ross got through with him. I figure I'm in the wrong dressing room. Well, I finally climb into the ring just before midnight. And by the time the referee, Arthur Donovan, raises my hand and calls me the new champion, it's 1:00 a.m. So, I guess, you could say it took me two days to win the bantamweight title."

A few years later Jeffra took off his championship robe in a title defense in the Garden and discovered that he had forgotten to put on his trunks. Jack Dempsey, who was his manager and in Jeffra's corner that night, said, "Harry, you'll do anything for a laugh." But Jeffra had the last laugh, as he donned his trunks and, with the Garden crowd totally behind a man who had proven himself so human, whipped his opponent easily.

John L. Sullivan was once asked by a reporter why he had never become a boxing instructor, a trade all other former pugilists had pursued.

"Well, son," the great John L. answered, "I tried it once. A husky young man took one lesson from me and went home a little the worse for wear. When he came around the second time he said, 'Mr. Sullivan, it was my idea to learn enough about boxing from you to be able to lick a certain young fellow I've got it in for. But I've changed my mind. If it's all the same to you, Mr. Sullivan, I'll just send this fellow down here to take the rest of my lessons for me.'"

Referees, Managers, Promoters & Others

1. Who was the only referee to work heavyweight championship bouts featuring Jersey Joe Walcott, Ezzard Charles, Joe Frazier, George Foreman, and Muhammad Ali?
2. What ex-heavyweight champion refereed more heavyweight championship bouts than any other?
3. What man refereed a heavyweight championship bout eight years previous to competing in one himself?
4. Who was the referee in the Robinson-Maxim light heavyweight championship bout?
5. Which famous referee's father was middleweight champion and held John L. Sullivan to a draw, although outweighed by 40 pounds?
6. What well-known trainer attended high school with Mario Lanza?
7. What manager was also a mink rancher?
8. What well-known ring announcer is the uncle of a family of entertainers?
9. What well-known ring announcer was a semiprofessional baseball player, brother of a sports writer, and an accom-

plished vocalist, who would, on occasion, sing the national anthem before a bout?

10. Who promoted the only championship bout scheduled for 23 rounds?
11. Who was the only ex-junior welterweight champion to referee a junior welterweight championship?
12. Who was the first referee to work a junior flyweight, junior featherweight, junior lightweight, junior welterweight, and junior middleweight championship bout?
13. Who was the promoter at the Portable A.C.?
14. What famous mystery writer was asked to referee the Jeffries-Johnson bout?
15. What champion retired and then refereed a bout between the two leading contenders for his vacated title?
16. Who was the only man to challenge unsuccessfully for the heavyweight championship and then later referee a heavyweight championshp bout?
17. The referee of the first light heavyweight championship bout later had a television series based on his life. Who was he?
18. Who refereed three welterweight championship bouts in three months?
19. When Archie Moore and Yvon Durelle fought a rematch for the light heavyweight championship in 1959, the location, the result, and the referee were the same as in their first bout. Who was the referee?
20. What famous referee was a rated lightweight boxer who competed in 55 bouts and never lost a decision, won or lost by foul, boxed a draw, or had any no-decision or no-contest bouts?
21. What ex-champion died in the ring while refereeing a bout?

REFEREES, MANAGERS, PROMOTERS & OTHERS [85]

22. Who was the first man to win the Al Buck Memorial Award as the Manager of the Year twice?
23. Babe Ruth was traded to the New York Yankees as an indirect result of the Jack Johnson-Jess Willard heavyweight championship bout. Explain.
24. Who was the only man to be in a heavyweight championship bout with Joe Louis, Ezzard Charles, Rocky Marciano, Sonny Liston, Floyd Patterson, and Muhammad Ali?
25. What man refereed a heavyweight championship bout at the age of 19?
26. What promoter grew up next to the ranch owned by the mother of Frank and Jesse James?
27. What champion's manager was a hypnotist?
28. Who is the only man to manage two world heavyweight champions?
29. What current National Hockey League team was named for a boxing promoter?

ANSWERS

1. *Zack Clayton refereed the Walcott defense against Charles on June 5, 1952, the Frazier defense against Ron Stander in 1972, and the Ali-Foreman bout in 1974.*

2. *While many ex-boxers have refereed bouts on occasion, only Jersey Joe Walcott and Jim Jeffries have won the heavyweight championship and have also refereed a heavyweight championship bout. Walcott refereed two bouts—the Ali-Liston second contest and the Patterson-McNeeley bout. Jeffries refereed heavyweight title bouts on four occasions. He refereed a contest between Marvin Hart and Jack Root to determine the successor to his own title after he vacated the championship; he refereed the bout in which Hart lost the title to Tommy Burns; and he refereed two of Burns's title defenses.*

3. *Georges Carpentier acted as third man in the ring for a bout between Jack Johnson and Andre Sproul in Paris in 1913. He also refereed the Johnson-Moran title fight the following year. In 1921, Carpentier challenged Jack Dempsey for the heavyweight title, but was unsuccessful.*

4. *On June 25, 1952, Sugar Ray Robinson met Joey Maxim in Yankee Stadium with Ruby Goldstein as the referee. The temperature reached 110 degrees under the lights in the ring, and Goldstein was felled by the heat in the twelfth round. Ray Miller replaced him, but did not have to work long, as Robinson succumbed to the heat shortly after and did not answer the bell for the fourteenth round.*

5. *Arthur Donovan, who refereed 14 heavyweight championship bouts—twice as many as any other man—was the son of Professor Mike Donovan. The Professor was middleweight champion during the bareknuckle era. He reigned from 1872 to 1882 and in that time twice boxed John L. Sullivan to a draw. He later also held Jack Dempsey, "The Nonpareil," to a draw. Among the Professor's other bouts was one in Cheyenne refereed by Wyatt Earp and another in San Francisco, which lasted 3 hours and 48 minutes over 96 rounds.*

6. *Angelo Dundee, trainer of Muhammad Ali, among others, attended high school in South Philadelphia with Mario Lanza, the singer.*

ANSWERS Referees, Managers, Promoters & Others

7. Marv Jensen, manager of the Fullmer brothers, was a successful mink farmer in West Jordan, Utah. Although the West Jordan population was only 1,800 in 1950, the town produced boxers such as Rex Layne, Olympic heavyweight Jay Lambert, and Jay, Don, and Gene Fullmer—thanks to the efforts of Jensen and the West Jordan AC.

8. Popular ring announcer Jimmy Lennon is the uncle of the Lennon sisters of Lawrence Welk television fame.

9. Johnny Addie was a fixture in New York City rings as ring announcer for more than 20 years. His brother, Bob Addie, was a columnist for the Washington Post.

10. James J. Coffroth was a California promoter around the turn of the century. On Labor Day, 1908, he promoted a bantamweight championship bout between Abe Attell and Owen Moran. This was the only world championship fight ever scheduled for 23 rounds. The two boxers had previously fought to a draw in a 25-round bout and this 23-rounder also ended in a draw.

11. Mushy Callahan was the second junior welterweight champion, reigning from 1926 to 1930. The class faded in interest during the mid 1930s and was not reactivated until 1959 when Carlos Ortiz became champion. In Ortiz's first defense against Battling Torres in Los Angeles in 1960, Mushy Callahan was the referee.

12. In 1976, Jay Edson, one of the busiest referees of all time, completed the cycle of junior championship bouts in which he has refereed. He has done third-man honors in junior flyweight, junior featherweight, junior lightweight, junior welterweight, and junior middleweight bouts. He has also refereed championship bouts in the heavyweight and welterweight classes.

13. The Portable A.C. was the name given to the shows promoted by James C. Mullen in Illinois during the 1920s, when boxing was illegal in Illinois. The reason for the name was that they sometimes took place at Aurora, Illinois; sometimes in East Chicago, Indiana, and sometimes even in Chicago itself. One of his promotions was a bout between baseball player Art (The Great) Shires and Notre Dame football player George Trafton.

14. Sir Arthur Conan Doyle, the creator of Sherlock Holmes, and a regular patron at the National Sporting Club of London boxing matches, was invited to referee the Jack Johnson-Jim Jeffries heavyweight championship bout by Tex Rickard, the promoter. Doyle refused and Rickard himself acted as referee.

15. James J. Jeffries, the heavyweight champion, ran out of opponents in 1905 and decided to retire. He named Marvin Hart and Jack Root as the two leading contenders for his title and personally refereed a bout between the two for his vacated title. Hart won by knockout in the twelfth round.

16. The referee for the Floyd Patterson-Pete Rademacher bout in Seattle in 1957 was Tommy Loughran. Loughran was light heavyweight champion from 1927 to 1929 and lost a 15-round decision to Primo Carnera for the heavyweight title in 1934. Georges Carpentier refereed a heavyweight championship bout before his unsuccessful challenge for the title.

17. Lou Houseman, the manager of Jack Root decided that Root was not quite large enough at 165 pounds to challenge the 215-pound Jim Jeffries for the heavyweight title, and so he matched Root with Kid McCoy for the championship of a new division with a 175-pound limit, which he called "light heavyweight." On April 22, 1903, Root won a 10-round decision from McCoy in Detroit to become the first light heavyweight champion, in a bout refereed by the legendary folk hero, Bat Masterson. In his first defense on July 4, 1903, Root lost his title to George Gardner.

18. Henry Armstrong defended his welterweight title more frequently than any other man. He defended it in each of the months of April, May, and June, 1940, with Johnny Martin as referee for all three bouts. Martin had little work, since none of the bouts lasted more than seven rounds.

19. Former heavyweight champion Jack Sharkey was the referee for both bouts, which were held in Montreal and ended with Moore winning by knockout.

20. Ruby Goldstein, known as the "Jewel of the Ghetto," was a lightweight contender from 1925 to 1937. His ring record is quite unusual in that he engaged in 55 bouts, won 34 by knockout, won 16 by decision, and was knocked out in the other 5 bouts. He is probably best known for his prowess as a referee and was the third man in the ring in seven heavyweight championship bouts.

21. Benny Leonard died April 18, 1947 after collapsing while refereeing a bout at St. Nicolas Arena, New York City. As was the custom in those days, Leonard was the sole referee for the entire card. In the year prior to Leonard's death, Young Otto, Harry Ebbets, and a man

ANSWERS Referees, Managers, Promoters & Others

named Goodman all collapsed while refereeing in New York, and in New Jersey referee Mickey Donley passed away from the strain of refereeing an entire card. As a result of these tragedies, two referees were required by New York State for all boxing shows.

22. Yancey Durham, the manager of Joe Frazier, received this award in both 1969 and 1971—the first man to win the award twice.

23. Harry Frazee was an incurable entrepreneur who dabbled in all manner of entertainment: Broadway shows, boxing bouts, wrestling matches, and baseball teams. He and Jack Curley promoted the Jack Johnson-Jim Flynn heavyweight championship in 1912 and the Johnson-Willard championship in 1915. They lost heavily on both bouts. In 1917, Frazee purchased the Boston Red Sox. By 1919, Frazee was desperately in need of money and borrowed from Jacob Ruppert, owner of the Yankees. On January 3, 1920, Ruppert called for the first installment of his loan and bought Babe Ruth from Frazee's Red Sox for $125,000

24. Jersey Joe Walcott lost two heavyweight championship bouts each to Joe Louis, Ezzard Charles, and Rocky Marciano and also defeated Charles for the title. He refereed the second Liston-Ali championship bout in Lewiston, Maine, in 1965 and also served as referee for Floyd Patterson's defense against Tom McNeeley in Toronto in 1961.

25. When Georges Carpentier refereed the Jack Johnson-Andre Sproul heavyweight championship bout in Paris in 1913, he was only 19 years old. He had been boxing professionally since he was 13 years old and had been the welterweight champion of Europe for two years at the time of the Johnson bout.

26. Tex Rickard started his life on a farm in Clay Country, Missouri, next to the one owned by Mrs. Zerelda Samuels, the mother of the notorious outlaws Frank and Jesse James.

27. James V. Grippo, the manager of the light heavyweight champion Melio Bettina, was a hypnotist who claimed his hypnotic ability played an important part in Bettina's success.

28. William A. Brady was the manager of James J. Corbett and James J. Jeffries. He also produced 260 Broadway plays, including the Pulitzer-Prize-winning Street Scene.

29. In 1926, while Tex Rickard was the promoter at Madison Square Garden, a hockey franchise was acquired by the Madison Square

Garden Corporation. The club, in a play on words, was called Tex's Rangers.

Places

1. What middleweight title bout was fought in two rings?
2. Who was the first African to win a middleweight championship?
3. Which light heavyweight champion was born in St. Louis, but did not box in the United States until after he won and lost the championship?
4. Who was the only heavyweight champion to win the championship in Madison Square Garden?
5. What arena hosted four heavyweight championship bouts, each of which resulted in a new champion?
6. What boxers boxed out of these places?
    a. Cut 'n' Shoot, Texas
    b. West Jordan, Utah
    c. Canastota, New York
    d. Louisville, Kentucky
    e. Brockton, Masschusetts
    f. Manassa, Colorado
    g. Gary, Indiana
    h. Pottawatomie County, Kansas
    i. Galveston, Texas
7. Through 1980, who was the only world champion to be born in these places?
    a. Austria
    b. Barbados
    c. Dominican Republic
    d. Greece
    e. New Zealand
    f. Nicaragua
    g. Senegal

h. Sweden
i. Switzerland
j. Virgin Islands
k. Yugoslavia

8. What famous bout occurred in these places?
   a. Shelby, Montana
   b. Lewiston, Maine
   c. Kinshasa, Zaire

9. Who is the only heavyweight champion never to box a heavyweight championship bout in the United States?

10. The nicknames of some boxers were derived from their home towns. Who were these boxers?
    a. The Herkimer Hurricane
    b. The Astoria Assassin
    c. The Casablanca Clouter
    d. The Pittsburgh Kid
    e. The Nebraska Wildcat
    f. The Michigan Assassin
    g. The Cleveland Rubber Man
    h. The Boston Strong Boy
    i. The Boston Tar Baby

11. By 1932, boxing in one form or another was legal in all 48 states except one. Which one?

12. Where was the first match held outside the United States which drew total gate receipts of more than $1,000,000?

13. What heavyweight champion boxed his first 17 professional bouts in Louisville, Kentucky?

14. How many bouts did Philadelphia Jack O'Brien actually have in Philadelphia?

15. In the movie *Rocky*, a heavyweight championship bout is held in Philadelphia. How many real life heavyweight championship bouts have been fought in Philly?

PLACES

16. Muhammad Ali was the first truly international champion. He boxed championship bouts in seven countries across four continents. How many of these places can you name?

17. In how many foreign countries did Archie Moore compete?

18. True or false? Although Joe Louis boxed exhibitions outside the United States, every one of his 71 regular bouts was held within the United States.

19. In what state was a bill proposed in the state legislature to prohibit boxing matches held in a four sided ring and instead require the ring to contain ten sides—to prevent boxers from being trapped in a corner?

20. Who won the first heavyweight championship bout to be held in Madison Square Garden?

21. Which middleweight champion fought his last bout on the island of Malta in the Mediterranean?

22. Who is the only "soul brother" to win a championship in Seoul, Korea?

ANSWERS

1. On December 13, 1887, Jack Dempsey, "The Nonpareil," defended his title against Johnny Reagan on Long Island. After four rounds the ring became submerged with water. The bout was moved 20 miles away and was finished in snow and cold in 1 hour and 13 minutes. Reagan was stopped in the forty-fifth round of this bareknuckle bout.

2. No, it was not Dick Tiger, but Marcel Cerdan, a native of Algeria in northern Africa, who defeated Tony Zale in 1948 to win the world middleweight championship. He lost his crown to Jake LaMotta the following year and shortly afterwards was killed in a plane crash while en route to the United States for a rematch with LaMotta.

3. Battling Siki, the Singular Senegalese, was born in St. Louis, Senegal, in West Africa and boxed in Europe from 1913 to 1923. He came to the United States in 1923 and boxed there until his death in 1925.

4. Joe Frazier won the New York State version of the heavyweight title by defeating Buster Mathis on March 4, 1968, in Madison Square Garden. He gained recognition by defeating Jimmy Ellis, the WBA champion on February 16, 1970, also in Madison Square Garden. He finally gained universal recognition by defeating Muhammad Ali on March 8, 1971. This bout was also held in Madison Square Garden. Through 1980, there have been 19 heavyweight championship bouts held in Madison Square Garden, more than in any other arena, but the title did not change hands in any of those other bouts.

5. During the 1930s the Madison Square Garden Corporation built an outdoor arena in Long Island City called the Madison Square Garden Bowl. There were only four heavyweight championship bouts held there, but all four resulted in a new heavyweight champion. On June 21, 1932, Jack Sharkey defeated Max Schmeling and became champion. In his first title defense Sharkey lost the title to Primo Carnera. Carnera defended twice successfully elsewhere, but then made the mistake of returning to the MSG Bowl and was knocked out by Max Baer. Baer's only defense was one year later, also in the Madison Square Garden Bowl, and he lost a 15-round decision to Jim Braddock.

ANSWERS Places

6.
   a. Roy Harris
   b. Gene, Don, and Jay Fullmer
   c. Carmen Basilio
   d. Muhammad Ali, Jimmy Ellis
   e. Rocky Marciano
   f. Jack Dempsey
   g. Tony Zale
   h. Jess Willard
   i. Jack Johnson

7.
   a. Elisha Obed, junior middleweight champion
   b. Joe Walcott, bantamweight champion
   c. Carlos (Teo) Cruz, lightweight champion
   d. David Kotey, featherweight champion
   e. Anton Christoforidis, light heavyweight champion
   f. Torpedo Billy Murphy, featherweight champion
   g. Alexis Arguello, featherweight and junior lightweight champion
   h. Battling Siki, light heavyweight champion
   i. Ingemar Johansson, heavyweight champion
   j. Frank Erne, lightweight champion
   k. Emile Griffith, welterweight and middleweight champion
   l. Mate Parlov, light heavyweight champion

8.
   a. Jack Dempsey-Tommy Gibbons, July 4, 1923
   b. Muhammad Ali-Sonny Liston, May 25, 1965
   c. Muhammad Ali-George Foreman, October 30, 1974

9. George Foreman was threatened with lawsuits while champion, and consequently all four of his championship bouts were contested outside the United States. He won the title from Joe Frazier in Kingston, Jamaica; defended against Jose (King) Roman in Tokyo and Ken Norton in Caracas, Venezuela; and lost the title to Muhammad Ali in Kinshasa, Zaire.

10.
    a. Lou Ambers
    b. Paul Berlenbach
    c. Marcel Cerdan
    d. Billy Conn
    e. Jack Dempsey
    f. Ace Hudkins
    g. Stanley Ketchel
    h. Eddie (Babe) Risko

i. *John L. Sullivan*
j. *Sam Langford*

11. *Texas was the only state in which boxing was not permitted. There were several other states in which boxing was permitted only when staged under the auspices of so-called "private clubs."*

12. *The Muhammad Ali-Joe Frazier bout in Manila, Philippines, on October 1, 1975, drew only 25,000 people, but with a top price of $200, a total gate of $1,600,000 was reached.*

13. *Although Muhammad Ali was Louisville's most famous fighter, his early bouts were boxed in Miami Beach, Las Vegas, New York, and Los Angeles, in addition to Louisville. Jimmy Ellis fought 13 of his first 14 bouts in Kentucky, with 11 of them in Louisville. But Marvin Hart of Jefferson County, Kentucky, boxed his first 18 bouts in Louisville and won 16 by knockout, 1 on a foul, and was knocked out in the other. Hart was heavyweight champion from July 3, 1905, until February 23, 1906.*

14. *Although O'Brien was somewhat of a globetrotter, with bouts in Fairbanks (Alaska), Dawson (Canada), and England, he was aptly named. He had 91 of his 186 bouts (including 5 exhibitions) in Philadelphia. He also had 14 other bouts in various other cities in Pennsylvania.*

15. *There have been six heavyweight championship bouts in Philadelphia. The last was in 1968 at the Spectrum, when Joe Frazier defeated Oscar Bonavena. The first was in 1909 between Jack Johnson and Philadelphia Jack O'Brien. The most famous was the first Jack Dempsey-Gene Tunney bout in 1926. Joe Louis-Gus Dorazio, Jersey Joe Walcott-Ezzard Charles (fourth bout), and Rocky Marciano-Jersey Joe Walcott (first bout) were the others.*

16. *Muhammad Ali boxed championship bouts in North America, Europe, Africa, and Asia. He defeated George Chuvalo in Toronto, Canada; Henry Cooper and Brian London in London, England; Karl Mildenberger in Frankfurt and Richard Dunn in Munich, Germany; Joe Bugner in Malaysia; Joe Frazier in Manila, Philippines; Jean-Pierre Coopman in San Juan, Puerto Rico; and George Foreman in Kinshasa, Zaire. He also boxed nontitle bouts in Japan, Ireland, Indonesia, and Switzerland.*

17. *Although Archie Moore did not have Ali's reputation as a globetrotter, Moore also competed in 11 foreign lands. He boxed in*

ANSWERS Places

Australia, Argentina, Canada, England, Germany, Italy, Mexico, Panama, Philippines, Uruguay, and Brazil.

18. True. Joe Louis fought exhibition tours in Canada, Mexico, Cuba, Central and South America, Japan, and Formosa, but never fought a regular bout outside the United States.

19. In 1963, after the death of Benny (Kid) Paret on national television, all sorts of proposals were made to make boxing safer. One such proposal was made in the South Carolina General Assembly. The author of the bill stated that "I don't believe that the outcome of a boxing match should be determined by the ability of one boxer to corner another in a 90-degree corner and beat him up." He proposed that the corners be widened to 144 degrees to make a ten-sided ring to allow boxers to slide out of corners and prevent undue advantages to the other boxer.

20. No one. On March 25, 1916, heavyweight champion Jess Willard boxed a 10-round heavyweight championship bout with Frank Moran. New York law did not permit decisions at that time, and the bout was recorded as "no decision," with Willard retaining his title.

21. Englishman Randy Turpin boxed his last bout in 1964 on the British colony of Malta. He knocked out his opponent in the second round.

22. Saoul Paul Mamby, a black boxer from the Bronx, New York, defeated Sang-Hyun Kim in Seoul, Korea, in February, 1980, to win the WBC junior welterweight championship.

Quotations

Identify the sources of these words:

1. "Let's go Chappie, we're going to have a lot of fun with that third strike."
2. "Corbett, Corbett, James J. Corbett, a truly great fighter."
3. "This was a man."
4. "He can run but he can't hide."
5. "We'll win because we're on God's side."
6. "Float like a butterfly, sting like a bee."
7. "I shoulda stood in bed."
8. "I can lick any SOB in the house."
9. "It is a good thing for a girl to learn to box. Poise, grace and buoyancy of movement result from this exercise."
10. "Must I finish him off, Mr. Angle?" "Box on."
11. "Master of the Noble Science of Defence on the right hand in Oxford Road near Adam & Eve court. Teaches Gentlemen the use of the small backsword and Quarterstaff at home & abroad."
12. "Whatever 'truculent' means, if it's good, then I'm that."
13. "Oye, Foreman boma ye."
14. "The bigger they are, the harder they fall."
15. "Always on the level, yours very truly, . . ."
16. "No shoes or boots with springs allowed."
17. "Goodnight, sweet prince."

18. "To see a white man really worrying about me changed my whole life."
19. "We wuz robbed."

ANSWERS

1. Joe Louis to his trainer, Jack Blackburn, in response to the comment that he had two strikes against him.

2. These were the last words attributed to Peter Jackson, the great black heavyweight at the turn of the century.

3. These are the words on the epitaph of Peter Jackson, who is buried in Toowong Cemetery in Australia.

4. Joe Louis, in reference to the fact that Billy Conn, the light heavyweight champion, was much faster than he was.

5. Although Joe Louis was not a talkative man, he produced some of the most intelligent and oft-quoted phrases. These words were in response to the question of who would win the Second World War. This is sometimes misquoted as "We'll win because God is on our side," which completely misses the point.

6. These were trainer Drew "Bundini" Brown's words of wisdom to Cassius Clay as he prepared to meet Sonny Liston for the heavyweight championship.

7. Joe Jacobs, the manager of Max Schmeling among others, was quoted as saying this one cold afternoon when he was talked into going to a baseball game.

8. This was the boast that John L. Sullivan would utter, usually after he had been drinking for a while.

9. These are the opening words of an article in the beauty column of the New York Evening World on February 27, 1905. The article is headed "The Model Maid Will Help Her Health by Boxing—A Half Hour a Day with the Gloves Will Give a Girl Self-Control, Buoyancy and Grace." The article is accompanied by five illustrations, including landing a blow on the chin, ducking a blow, and a blow to the solar plexus.

10. Peter Jackson, in his bout against Frank Slavin, was winning overwhelmingly and didn't wish to inflict permanent injury. He attempted to convince Slavin to quit, but Slavin continued stoically. Finally, Jackson turned to the referee, Mr. Angle, and asked him to terminate the bout. But by the rules of that time, he was not permitted to do so.

ANSWERS Quotations

11. This was the card of James Figg, the first heavyweight champion and proprietor of a boxing school.

12. Muhammad Ali, in response to Howard Cosell's comment that he was becoming extremely truculent during a television interview.

13. Elmo Henderson, one of George Foreman's sparring partners, would constantly bellow this phrase during the preparations for the Foreman-Ali bout in Zaire. It translates to "Hear Ye, Foreman will kill him." The chant of "Ali boma ye" was also heard from Ali partisans during that bout.

14. These words were spoken by Bob Fitzsimmons, the 167-pound heavyweight champion, in reference to his forthcoming bout against Jim Jeffries who outweighed him by 50 pounds. Budd Schulberg used the last four of these words as the title of his book, which was later made into a motion picture.

15. John L. Sullivan would often make brief speeches after winning a bout and always concluded them with "always on the level, yours very truly, John L. Sullivan."

16. This is number 11 of the 12 original Marquess of Queensberry rules governing boxing.

17. Although William Shakespeare first wrote these words, sportscaster Sal Marchiano has popularized this phrase when a boxer is knocked out.

18. Ron Lyle was seriously wounded in a prison knife fight. When he came to, he saw Lt. Cliff Mattax, the prison athletic director, at his bedside. Lyle spoke these words in a subsequent interview.

19. Undoubtedly, many boxing managers have uttered these words, but Joe Jacobs is credited with this quote after Schmeling lost the heavyweight title to Jack Sharkey.

Writers and Boxing Literature

1. Who wrote the Marquess of Queensberry rules?
2. The author of *The Poseidon Adventure* played a large role in amateur boxing. Who was he and what did he do?
3. Many boxers have written their autobiographies after their retirement from the ring. Who were the authors of these autobiographies?
   a. Somebody Up There Likes Me
   b. Raging Bull
   c. Monkey on My Back
   d. Gloves, Glory and God
   e. The Greatest
   f. Weigh-In
   g. Fighting for Fun
   h. Will to Conquer
   i. Roar of the Crowd
4. What boxing writer and one-time sports editor of the New York *Sun* has the same name as a knuckleball relief pitcher of the 1970s?
5. The most famous poem about boxing is "The Nonpareil's Grave." Who was it about and who wrote it?
6. What heavyweight champion was known for his poetry?
7. What boxer wrote his autobiography, had it privately published, and, although selling it personally, had 17 editions printed?
8. Some of the world's greatest writers have also written of the prize ring in various forms. Identify these great writers:

WRITERS AND BOXING LITERATURE [103]

    a. a nineteenth-century French novelist, author of *Les Miserables,* who, in one of his other novels, wrote of a boxing match between an Irishman named Phelem-Ghe-Madone and a Scotchman named Helmsgail.
    b. a twentieth-century short-story writer famous for his surprise endings, who wrote a boxing short story called "The Higher Pragmatism"
    c. an American Nobel-Prize winner who wrote "Fifty Grand"
    d. an ancient Greek epic poet who may have been the first boxing writer
    e. an early twentieth century American novelist, Alaskan adventurer, journalist, and occasional boxing correspondent
    f. a nineteenth century British mystery writer, author of a novel about boxing and a short story called "The Croxley Master"
    g. a British Nobel-Prize-winning playwright who wrote five unsuccessful novels, including one about boxing called *Cashel Byron's Profession*
    h. a British poet who wrote a poem about the Heenan-Sayers bout
    i. an American Pulitzer-Prize-winning writer whose works include a biography of Marilyn Monroe, a famous war novel, and a comprehensive account of the Ali-Foreman bout

9. Who was the author of the first published boxing rules?

10. Who was the most prolific twentieth century boxing writer and historian?

11. One of the most famous sports cartoonists was TAD. What did TAD stand for?

12. One of the few plays dealing with boxing to be successful on Broadway was *Golden Boy.* Who wrote it?

13. *The Great White Hope* was the first play about boxing to win the Pulitzer Prize. Who wrote it?

14. Who was Pierce Egan and what significance does he have in the boxing world?
15. Who was the first man to win both the Nat Fleischer Memorial Award and the James J. Walker Award?
16. What biblical writer had the same name as a middleweight of the 1940s?

ANSWERS

1. John Sholto Douglas, the eighth Marquess of Queensberry, could be called the Abner Doubleday of boxing. He is generally credited with molding the sport into its present-day form, yet he did not write the rules generally attributed to him. John Graham Chambers wrote them in 1865 and requested that the Marquess sponsor them. As the sponsor, the Marquess has achieved undeserved fame, while the true author, Chambers, has been given no recognition.

2. Paul Gallico, who wrote The Poseidon Adventure and many other works, was originally sports editor of the New York Daily News during the 1920s. In February of 1927 he organized an amateur boxing tournament in which the winners would receive a miniature pair of golden gloves. The response was overwhelming, and nearly 500 contestants took part in 16 different classes. The tournament has continued uninterrupted since, with over 30,000 boxers competing in that time.

3. **a.** Rocky Graziano
   b. Jake La Motta
   c. Barney Ross
   d. Henry Armstrong
   e. Muhammad Ali
   f. Frazer Scott
   g. Eddie Eagan
   h. Mickey Walker
   i. James J. Corbett

4. Wilbur Wood was one of the best-known boxing writers of the 1930s. His namesake was a star relief pitcher for the Chicago White Sox during the 1970s.

5. Middleweight champion Jack Dempsey, "The Nonpareil," died in 1895 at the age of 32. M. J. McMahon of Portland, Oregon, Dempsey's lawyer, was so disturbed by the neglect of his idol's grave that he wrote a poem and circulated 1,000 copies of it anonymously. It was published in a Portland newspaper in 1899. Dempsey's friends later erected a tombstone, on which the poem is inscribed.

6. Muhammad Ali, in his years as Cassius Clay, the heavyweight contender, would write poems predicting the demise of his opponents before each bout. A sample, written prior to the bout with Archie Moore:

> Archie had been living off the fat of the land
> I'm here to give him his pension plan
> When you come to the fight don't block aisle or door
> 'Cause y'all going home after round four.

(He did stop Moore in four rounds.)

7. Abraham Hollandersky, known as Abe the Newsboy, started boxing in 1905 and through 1918 was credited with 1,039 boxing and wrestling matches—far more than any other man. His biography, *The Life Story of Abe the Newsboy—Hero of a Thousand Fights,* was privately published (the publisher is listed simply as "Published by Abe the Newsboy, Los Angeles, California"). The 538-page volume was initially published in 1930 and through 1953 was printed in 17 editions.

8.
   a. *Victor Hugo in* The Man Who Laughs
   b. *O. Henry*
   c. *Ernest Hemingway*
   d. *Homer, who wrote* The Iliad, *which contains a section describing a boxing match*
   e. *Jack London*
   f. *Sir Arthur Conan Doyle, the creator of Sherlock Homes*
   g. *George Bernard Shaw*
   h. *William Makepeace Thackeray*
   i. *Norman Mailer, who wrote* The Fight

9. *Jack Broughton, in 1743, drew up the first set of boxing rules, which included "That no person is to hit his adversary when he is down, or seize him by the hair, the breeches, or any part below the waist; a man on his knees to be reckoned down."*

10. *Nat Fleischer, the founder of* The Ring *and creator of* The Ring Record Book, *and author of more than 50 books on boxing, did more for the sport than any nonboxer ever.*

11. *Thaddeus Aloysius Dorgan.*

12. *Clifford Odets wrote this play, which was first performed on Broadway in 1937.*

13. *Howard Sackler won the Pulitzer Prize for his play about Jack Johnson.*

14. *Pierce Egan was the nineteenth century boxing writer whose monthly publication,* Boxiana, *was the first periodical devoted to the sport. He was the first man to make a career of sports writing and was boxing's first historian.*

15. *The Nat Fleischer Memorial Award is presented by the Boxing Writers' Association of New York to the person who has done the most for boxing in covering that sport during the preceding year. Barney Nagler was the first recipient of this award in 1972. He was also awarded the James J. Walker Memorial Award for long and meritorious service to boxing in 1973.*

16. *During the 1940s a light heavyweight boxer billed solely as St. Paul appeared in New England rings. In bouts from 1944 to 1949, the Saint compiled a record of 41-29-2. Fortunately for Christianity, the original Saint Paul had a far better won-lost record.*

Movies, Television, Radio, and Theater

1. What actor portrayed a lefthanded boxer in the 1939 film *They Made Me a Criminal* and then turned around and boxed righthanded in a 1947 film for which he received an Academy Award nomination?
2. What was the name of the 1956 film that was loosely based on the life of a real-life heavyweight champion and starred Humphrey Bogart as a boxing reporter?
3. On whose life was that film based?
4. What ex-heavyweight champion had a featured role in the film?
5. Name the heavyweight champion who, while champion, played the lead role in a television dramatization of a story written by Ernest Hemingway?
6. What was the first film about boxing to win the Academy Award for Best Picture?
7. Which Academy-Award-winning actor went the distance in a real-life heavyweight championship bout?
8. What boxer starred in the film *Huckleberry Finn*?
9. Can you name the boxer who starred in the film *Freedom Road*?
10. What boxer played the part of Sylvester Stallone's brother in the film *Paradise Alley*?

MOVIES, TELEVISION, RADIO, AND THEATER [109]

11. What champion retired from boxing to become a professional entertainer and later came out of retirement to regain his championship and box for 13 more years?

12. A boxer, once ranked eighth in *The Ring's* annual ratings, became a Shakespearean actor. Can you name him?

13. Rocky Marciano defeated Joe Louis in their real-life bout. Yet the actor who played the part of Joe Louis in the film *The Joe Louis Story* defeated Rocky Marciano as an amateur. Who was that actor?

14. What heavyweight champion had the lead role in the Broadway play *Big Time Buck White*?

15. The play and the movie *The Great White Hope* were based on the life of what boxer?

16. Who played the lead in both the play and the movie?

17. Who starred in the original *Kid Galahad*?

18. What singer played the lead role in the remake of that film?

19. Who was the first heavyweight champion who *didn't* appear in a Broadway show?

20. In the film *Rocky* the heavyweight champion was played by a real-life professional athlete. Who was he and what sport did he play?

21. When were the first motion pictures of a boxing match made?

22. When were the first 3-D motion pictures of a boxing match taken?

23. The Playhouse 90 television production of *Requiem for a Heavyweight* is a classic. The lead roles were a boxer, his manager, and his trainer. Who played these three parts?

24. What was unusual about the actor who played the trainer?

25. Who played those roles in the film version?

26. Also appearing in the film were two of the greatest heavyweights of all time. Who were they?
27. The story *Golden Boy* is another classic. Who starred in the film?
28. Who starred in the Broadway production?
29. What was different about the "remake" of the original Broadway production?
30. A popular television show during the 1950s was "You'll Never Get Rich" later called "The Phil Silvers Show." Phil Silvers played Sergeant Bilko and included in his platoon was a top-ranked middleweight boxer. Who was he?
31. One of the stars of the television series "Taxi" is a New York middleweight boxer with a string of one-round knockouts to his credit. Who is he?
32. What biographical boxing film starred two Academy Award winners, four other actors who had received Academy Award nominations, and was written by an Academy-Award-winning writer?
33. Identify these films about boxing from these capsule descriptions.
    a. A press agent exposes the crooked fight game.
    b. A Guadalcanal hero is given morphine to relieve malaria and becomes addicted.
    c. An East Side kid with reform school experience becomes middleweight champion.
    d. The rise to fame of boxer Jim Corbett.
    e. A young boxer fights his way unscrupulously to the top.
    f. A boxer falls for a high-class gangster's girl
    g. An ambitious prizefighter alienates his friends and family, and dies of injuries received in the ring.
    h. A Philadelphia boxer makes good.
    i. A poor boy is torn between two absorbing interests: prizefighting and playing the violin.

MOVIES, TELEVISION, RADIO, AND THEATER [111]

   j. The last bouts of a professional who will not realize his career is over.
   k. In New Orleans in the depression-hit 30s, a prizefighter and a promoter help each other.
   l. In 1910, a black boxer becomes world heavyweight champion but has trouble through his affair with a white woman.

34. What boxing film was completed in 20 days at a cost of $500,000 and earned more than $2,000,000 in the United States alone?

35. From what boxing film did a song receive an Academy Award nomination as Best Song?

36. Who was the first radio broadcaster for a boxing match?

37. In the 1950s, comedienne Martha Raye had a weekly television show. An ex-boxer appeared as a regular on that show. Who was he?

ANSWERS

1. The ambidextrous John Garfield received an Academy Award nomination for Best Actor for his role in the 1947 film Body and Soul.

2. The Harder They Fall by Budd Schulberg starred Humphrey Bogart, in his last film, as a boxing reporter following the career of boxer Toro Moreno, as played by Mike Lane.

3. The story was loosely based on Primo Carnera's rise to the heavyweight championship.

4. Jersey Joe Walcott had a featured role as a trainer in that film.

5. Ingemar Johansson played the lead in the television production of "The Killers" based on the Hemingway story.

6. Although there have been several classic films about boxing such as Body and Soul and Champion, the first to win the Academy Award for Best Picture was Rocky in 1976.

7. Victor McLaglen met heavyweight champion Jack Johnson on March 10, 1909, in Vancouver, B. C., in the first world heavyweight championship bout held in Canada. The bout went the limit of six rounds and was scored as no-decision. McLaglen became a successful actor and in 1935 won the Academy Award for Best Actor for his performance in The Informer.

8. Archie Moore had a starring role in the film Huckleberry Finn.

9. Muhammad Ali had a featured role in the made-for-television film, Freedom Road.

10. Lee Canalito has had only limited success in the ring, but gave an excellent performance as Sylvester Stallone's brother in Paradise Alley.

11. Sugar Ray Robinson gave up his middleweight title on December 18, 1952, to pursue a career as a song-and-dance man, but after nearly 2 years decided that he would be more successful as a boxer. He made the right decision, as he regained his championship and boxed for 11 more years.

12. Canada Lee was The Ring's eighth-ranked welterweight in 1929. After retiring from the ring, he became an actor and starred in the Broadway play Native Son. He received critical acclaim for his

ANSWERS *Movies, Television, Radio, and Theater* [113]

performance in the lead role of the film Cry, the Beloved Country. He also performed in various Shakespearean productions.

13. Coley Wallace was a very successful amateur boxer. Included in his titles were the New York, Eastern Regional, and Intercity Golden Gloves championships in 1948. In the Eastern Regional Golden Gloves, he defeated Rocky Marciano in a preliminary bout in the tournament.

14. While Muhammad Ali was battling the U.S. Government, he appeared in the lead role of a short-lived (seven performances) Broadway play called Big Time Buck White, which opened on December 2, 1970.

15. The Great White Hope was based on the life of Jack Johnson.

16. James Earl Jones played the lead in both the film and the play. He received an Academy Award nomination and won the 1969 Tony award for his performance as Jack Johnson, the heavyweight champion. Jane Alexander also received the Tony award and an Academy Award nomination for her role.

17. The original Kid Galahad was Wayne Morris.

18. Elvis Presley starred in the remake of Kid Galahad.

19. The first heavyweight champion who did not appear in a Broadway show was Marvin Hart. John L. Sullivan, Jim Corbett, Bob Fitzsimmons, and Jim Jeffries all appeared in Broadway shows.

20. The role of Apollo Creed, the heavyweight champion, was played by ex-professional football player Carl Weathers. Weathers was a linebacker for the Oakland Raiders in 1970 and 1971.

21. The first use of a motion picture machine to film fighters in action was the Edison Kinetoscope at the Edison Laboratories, Llewellyn, New Jersey. It was filmed in the Kinetographic Theatre, known as the Black Maria, the first movie house. It was painted black, both inside and out, and could be revolved on its base to follow the sunlight. As a test, Thomas Edison had Mike Leonard and Jack Cushing, both of Brooklyn, New York, appear at the laboratories to engage in an exhibition of six rounds. This took place on June 16, 1894. At the conclusion of the bout, a warrant for the arrest of the principals was issued for engaging in a prize fight in violation of the law.

22. The first motion pictures of a boxing match in three dimensions (3-D) was Rocky Marciano-Jersey Joe Walcott world heavyweight title bout at Chicago, May 15, 1953. This was also one of the last motion pictures of a boxing match in 3-D; that medium did not last long.

23. Requiem for a Heavyweight was the second production of the "Playhouse 90" television series. It was first telecast on October 11, 1956, and starred Jack Palance as the boxer, Keenan Wynn as his manager, and Ed Wynn as his trainer. Max Baer and Maxie Rosenbloom also had supporting roles.

24. This was the first dramatic appearance for the famous comedian Ed Wynn, who was 70 years old at that time.

25. Six years later a film of Requiem was produced by David Susskind for Columbia Pictures. It was directed by Ralph Nelson and starred Anthony Quinn as the boxer, comedian Jackie Gleason as his manager, and Mickey Rooney as the trainer.

26. Both Jack Dempsey and Cassius Clay (as he was then known) had supporting roles in the film.

27. The film Golden Boy was produced by William Perlberg and directed by Rouben Mamoulian. It was a Columbia Pictures production and starred Barbara Stanwyck, William Holden, Adolph Menjou, Joseph Calleia, and Lee J. Cobb.

28. Golden Boy was originally presented on the Broadway stage in 1937. Luther Adler, Lee J. Cobb, Elia Kazan, and Karl Malden played the leading roles.

29. It was a musical version of Golden Boy. It starred Sammy Davis, Jr., Paula Wayne, and Billy Daniels. It ran for 569 performances from October 20, 1964 through March 5, 1966.

30. Walter Cartier was a regular member of Sergeant Bilko's platoon. He boxed from 1946 to 1954, and then, while acting on the show, attempted a comeback in 1957. He retired permanently after only two bouts that year, with a lifetime record of 45-13-2 as a top-rated middleweight.

31. Tony Danza has been a regular on "Taxi" since its inception. He has also maintained his ring career while acting. Through 1979 he won 8, all by knockout, was knocked out twice, and lost one decision. Six of his eight knockouts came in the first round.

32. The 1977 film The Greatest, based on the life of Muhammad Ali, had one of the greatest casts ever to appear in a film about boxers. Ernest Borgnine and Ben Johnson, as well as James Earl Jones, Paul

ANSWERS *Movies, Television, Radio, and Theater* [115]

Winfield, Robert Duvall, and John Marley, all appeared. Borgnine and Johnson were Academy Award winners and Jones, Winfield, Duvall, and Marley were all Academy Award nominees. The screenplay was written by Ring Lardner, Jr., also an Academy Award winner. None of these awards or nominations were for the *The Greatest*.

33.
  a. *They Harder They Fall*
  b. *Monkey on My Back*
  c. *Somebody Up There Likes Me*
  d. *Gentleman Jim*
  e. *Body and Soul*
  f. *The Prizefighter and the Lady*
  g. *Champion*
  h. *Rocky*
  i. *Golden Boy*
  j. *Requiem for a Heavyweight*
  k. *Hard Times*
  l. *The Great White Hope*

34. *Champion*, produced by Stanley Kramer and directed by Mark Robson, starred Kirk Douglas, Arthur Kennedy, and Marilyn Maxwell. Academy Award nominations were received by Douglas, Kennedy, the writer Carl Foreman, the photographer Franz Planer, and Dmitri Tiomkin for the music.

35. The song "Gonna Fly Now" which was the theme from *Rocky*, and was written by Bill Conti with lyrics by Carol Connors and Ayn Robbins, received a nomination for the Best Song even though it did not have many lyrics. It was, however, a powerful theme.

36. Jack Dempsey, the heavyweight champion, reported the Georges Carpentier-Ted (Kid) Lewis bout on May 11, 1922, from the Olympic Club in London, by wireless telephone. Dempsey didn't have a chance to say much as Carpentier stopped Lewis in the first round.

37. Rocky Graziano became a television star as the "Goombah" of Martha Raye on her weekly television show. He now specializes in commercials.

Time Out

Rocky Marciano, former undefeated heavyweight champ, was known for his pinchpenny habits, even, it was rumored, going to the trouble of burying his money in potato fields, much like W. C. Fields before him. One time Marciano came to see the matchmaker at Madison Square Garden for a dozen tickets for a big show the Garden was putting on. For free, of course! The matchmaker struck a bargain with the Rock. He'd let him have a dozen comps on one condition: that he not come back for any more. But, sure enough, the day before the fight, Marciano returned with a request for an additional six. The matchmaker would not budge on his end of the arrangement. There would be no more "Annie Oakleys" for Marciano.

"I do have something for you, champ," the matchmaker said, opening a drawer. "Here's your check for the royalties you earned on your last title fight." He handed Marciano a check for $9,000.

Marciano gratefully accepted the check, admonishing the matchmaker not to tell his former manager, who would want a piece of the action, and moved towards the door. Then he stopped and turned around. "How 'bout those tickets?"

He got them.

Bernard Gimbel, the department store mogul, who followed the fights almost as avidly as he did Macy's competitive sales, was called boxing's Number One Fan. It was a title he won the night of the famous Tunney-Dempsey "Long Count" bout in Chicago back in 1927. Somehow or other, even with a phalanx of special police guarding the victorious Tunney and his dressing room, Gimbel managed to wangle his way in.

"The next thing I knew," an astonished Tunney was later to relate, "there was Bernie, fully clothed, including raincoat and hat, standing happily under the shower with me, talking a mile a minute about the fight."

Norman Selby, who fought under the name "Kid McCoy," may well have been the most colorful performer ever to enter the squared circle. It was Selby who gave rise to the phrase "The real McCoy." Seems he was out with a pretty blonde friend one night when a drunk made a pass at her. Refusing to believe the fighter's credentials, the drunk persisted, but when he came to with a swollen jaw, he allowed as how his opponent was, indeed, The Real McCoy.

McCoy also invented the famous "Corkscrew punch." But he was as much a corkscrew himself as the punch he invented.

McCoy was once fighting a South African named Equator, because he was so big around the middle. The big African not only weighed some 350 pounds, but also stood 6 feet, 8 inches tall and fought barefooted. For one round Equator ran McCoy dizzy, his bare feet slapping the canvas like a Mississippi side-wheeler. Before the second round McCoy threw half a dozen tacks into the ring and as his opponent reached down to investigate the strange prickle on his feet, McCoy brought up a Maryanne to the jaw and ended the match.

Another time he was matched with a dangerous opponent who just happened to be stone deaf. McCoy became aware of his adversary's affliction near the end of the third round and immediately went into action, stepping back a pace and indicating, in pantomine, that the bell had sounded, marking the end of the round. Actually, it had not. Nevertheless, his deaf opponent muttered "Thanks" and dropped his hands, whereupon McCoy knocked him out with a straight right.

When the Publicist of Madison Square Garden was told by one of Chalky Wright's followers that the featherweight champion was a lover of classical music, he managed to fold it into a press release. The next thing he heard, a reporter from Etude, the music magazine, went up to interview Wright for a story.

"Mr. Wright," the reporter asked, "What is your opinion of Mozart?" Chalky answered, "Well, I find him a little heavy." "Is that so, Mr. Wright?" said the reporter. "You're probably the only person in the world who ever found Mozart heavy. What about Bach? "A very clever boy," Wright responded, without missing a beat. "Can't miss." The reporter then invoked the name of Beethoven. "Dynamite!" said the champ.

After the interview, Wright came to find the publicist and told him, "You got me in a mess of trouble."

Boxing has always had celebrity status. Especially among its sports writers. Many is the time a special correspondent was assigned to cover a boxing match, just as the New York Post assigned Charles Francis Coe, lawyer, criminologist, and novelist of the-then best-selling book Me . . . Gangster, to cover the 1931 heavyweight title fight between Max Schmeling and Young Stribling in Cleveland. The fight was no fight, with Schmeling dominating his challenger in what was, at best, a dull contest, and finally knocking him out in the fifteenth round.

Coe's account of the fight: "Cleveland, July 3—I saw nothing to write about in the Max Schmeling-Young Stribling fight."

Period, end of story.

Tony Pellone, once a ranking welterweight out of the Greenwich Village section of New York City, had a unique method of handling his money. "I take it home to my old man," Pellone explained to one curious writer. "At first I didn't make much, but I'd give it to my old man and he'd give me five dollars out of it.

"One time I fought Bob Montgomery in the Garden and got $8,513 for my end. So I took it home and gave it to my old man. And he said, in Italian, 'How you fixed?' And I told him the truth. 'I'm broke,' I said. 'All right,' he said. 'Here,' and handed me thirteen dollars. 'What's this?,' I asked. 'Whatsa matter, you superstitious?' he asked and took one dollar back. 'There, that's twelve. Now not unlucky for you.'"

Scoring

1. In what bout was the referee's scorecard not counted?
2. What 1950s bout was scored as a no-decision because the referee used one scoring system while the judges used another?
3. What man lost his championship by decision because he was penalized for five rounds for foul blows?
4. In what bout was the decision reversed by the State Supreme Court?
5. When was the first bout in which the details of the official scoring were announced by the ring announcer?
6. What championship bout was scored 3-2 and 10 even?
7. What was the most even championship bout?

ANSWERS

1. When Carmen Basilio met Chuck Davey on May 29, 1952, in Syracuse, the referee scored the bout even 3-3-4. He neglected to use the supplementary point scoring which New York State requires in the event of a draw. Basilio was originally declared the winner, but the New York State Athletic Commission eventually tossed the referee's card out and based the revised decision on the cards of the two judges, with the result being a draw.

2. Scoring during the 1950s was going through an evolution with many different point systems used by different states. In the Joey Giardello-Willie Vaughn middleweight bout in Kansas City, Missouri, in 1957, the bout was scored under the 5-point-must system (the winner of a round receives 5 points and the loser 4 points or less). The referee inadvertently scored the bout under the 10 point divisible system (the winner gets 6 points or more and the loser gets 4 points or less). Although Vaughn was the winner by a split decision no matter which system was used, the Missouri Athletic Commission later declared the referee's card void and the bout officially was recorded as ending in "no decision."

3. Henry Armstrong, welterweight and lightweight champion, defended his lightweight title against Lou Ambers on August 22, 1939. Ambers won a unanimous decision although on two of the three scorecards it was only by an 8-7 margin. Armstrong was penalized by referee Art Donovan for foul punches and Ambers was awarded the 2nd, 5th, 7th, 9th, and 11th rounds.

4. Giardello figured in another scoring controversy in his bout against Billy Graham on December 19, 1952. The referee scored the bout 5-4-1 for Giardello, one judge scored it 7-3 for Graham, and judge Joe Agnello scored it 6-4- for Giardello. New York State commissioners Bob Christenberry and C.B. Powell at ringside changed Agnello's card to 5-5 in rounds and 6-5 in points for Graham and awarded the bout to Graham. Three months later, State Supreme Court Justice Bernard Botein in New York City ruled that the Commission had no right to reverse the scorecard of the official and declared the actual decision to be that originally given—in favor of Giardello.

In a 12-round rematch held on March 6, 1953, Graham won a decision.

ANSWERS Scoring

5. The Tippy Larkin-Lulu Costantino lightweight bout at Madison Square Garden, New York, on February 9, 1944, was the first time that the breakdown of the officials' cards were announced over the loudspeaker. Instead of merely announcing "Winner—Larkin," The announcer, George Kobb, gave the breakdown as "Judge Joe Agnello, 9-1 for Larkin, Judge Sam Robinson, 8-2 for Larkin, Referee Arthur Susskind (Young Otto), 9-1 for Larkin, winner by unanimous decision—Tippy Larkin."

6. Ringside judge Angelo Poletti scored the first Leonard-Duran bout 148-47 for Duran using the 10-point-must system. Translated, this means that of the maximum 150 points that a boxer could receive, Duran only lost 2 rounds and Leonard only lost 3 rounds. Since there were 15 rounds in the bout, Poletti must have scored the other 10 rounds even.

It was said by some that the reason that only 10 rounds were scored even was that Poletti ran out of fingers.

7. The WBC light flyweight title bout on March 31, 1979, in Seoul, Korea, between champion Kim Sung-Jun of Korea and challenger Hector Melendez of the Dominican Republic, was the most even championship bout ever. The neutral American referee scored it 3 rounds each and 9 even; the Korean judge scored it 4-2 for Kim with 9 rounds even and the South American judge scored it 6-2 for Melendez with 7 rounds even. The decision, of course, was a draw.

The Ring Ratings

All questions in this chapter are based on the annual ratings as published by *The Ring*

1. Who was the only man to be the number one challenger in two divisions simultaneously?
2. Who were the only number one-ranked heavyweights who never got a title bout?
3. In 1963, the top ten heavyweights had something in common besides being top-ranked heavyweights. What was it?
4. What was the only year in which both the heavyweight and light heavyweight championships were vacant?
5. What were the only two consecutive years in which the heavyweight championship was vacant?
6. In what year were the most heavyweight champions or future heavyweight champions rated among the top ten heavyweights?
7. As of 1980, who was the last light heavyweight champion to be rated among the top ten heavyweights?
8. Who was the only light heavyweight champion to also be rated as the number one heavyweight contender while champion?
9. Who was the only ex-welterweight champion to be rated among the top ten heavyweights?
10. In what year was the champion and four of the top ten ranked boxers in his division all named Joe?
11. In which two consecutive years were three of the eight titles vacant?
12. In what year were four of eight titles vacant?

THE RING RATINGS

13. What were the most consecutive years without a title vacancy?
14. What were the most consecutive years with a title vacant?
15. In what years did the champion and number one-rated challenger bear the same last name?
16. What was the only year that *The Ring* recognized co-champions?
17. From 1925 to 1942, *The Ring* ratings showed the title vacant in one class for 15 of those 18 years. What was that class?
18. What two men were champion and number one challenger for six consecutive years?
19. In what year was a champion ranked fourth?
20. In 1934, the top two rated welterweights were men who would box for a combined total of 62 years, but neither ever received a world title shot. Who were these men?
21. What rated boxer had the shortest full name?
22. Who were the only men to compete in heavyweight championship bouts (since 1924) that were never ranked among the top ten in the annual ratings?
23. In what year did the heavyweight ratings include a Big Boy, a Bobo, and a Turkey?
24. What heavyweight contender, once ranked third, finally got a title shot after four years of not being rated among the top ten?
25. Name the heavyweight champion who was unranked in all the years prior to his winning the championship?
26. What two boxers were ranked in 17 consecutive years from 1945 to 1961?
27. In what class was M. Ali the number one challenger in 1960?

28. What weight class was included from 1924 to 1931 and then disappeared until 1962?

29. What world champion was never rated higher than sixth in the annual ratings?

30. Who was the number one lightweight in 1951, who was never ranked in the top ten in any other year?

31. What "unknown" boxer first made his appearance in the 1932 ratings?

32. In 1972, the champion and three of the top five rated boxers in one division were ex-Olympic champions. Who were these four men?

33. What 17-year-old with a record for 42-1 was the number 10 bantamweight in 1976?

34. What brothers were rated in the same division in the same year?

35. Three boxers were included among the top ten middleweights in 1940 and each would later become a number one heavyweight challenger. Who are they?

36. What heavyweight started boxing professionally in 1932, but did not appear in the annual ratings until 1951—20 years after he started his career?

37. The top ten heavyweights in 1957 shared a unique distinction that has never been repeated. What was that?

ANSWERS

1. In 1942, Jimmy Bivins was rated as the top challenger for Joe Louis's heavyweight title, as well as the top challenger for Gus Lesnevich's light heavyweight title. Bivins was called the "Interim heavyweight champion" during the years when Joe Louis was in the service, but he was never fortunate enough to receive a title shot in any division and closed his career with a creditable record of 86-25-1.

2. In addition to Jimmy Bivins, who was the number one contender in 1942 and 1943, Melio Bettina, Steve Hamas, Harry Wills, and Nino Valdes were the only boxers to be rated number one and never receive a title bout. Hamas was top rated in 1934, Wills in 1924-25, Bettina in 1944, and Valdes in 1953-54.

3. All ten of the heavyweights rated in the top ten in 1963 received title bouts at some point in their careers. This was the first time since The Ring ratings were first published in 1924 that this occurred. Eight of the ten faced Muhammad Ali for the title and the other two had bouts with Ernie Terrell for the WBA crown.

4. In 1929, both the light heavyweight and heavyweight titles were vacant at year end. A successor to Gene Tunney had not yet emerged, and Tommy Loughran, the light heavyweight champion, had abandoned his title to box as a heavyweight.

5. Gene Tunney announced his retirement in August, 1928. It was not until June, 1930, that Max Schmeling became the next heavyweight champion.

6. In 1972, six of the top ten rated heavyweights were or would become heavyweight champion. Included in the ratings in that year when Joe Frazier was champion were: Muhammad Ali, number one; George Foreman, number two; Jimmy Ellis, number three; Floyd Patterson, number five; Ernie Terrell, number six; and Ken Norton, number nine.

7. There has not been a light heavyweight champion rated among the top ten heavyweights since Archie Moore was the ninth-rated contender in 1962.

8. Only Archie Moore earned that distinction in 1955.

9. Mickey Walker was the welterweight champion in 1924. By

1930, he was boxing heavyweights and was considered the number five contender in that division.

10. In 1946, Joe Louis was still heavyweight champion. Jersey Joe Walcott was the third-ranked contender. The eighth-, ninth-, and tenth-rated heavyweights were Joe Baksi, Joe Kahut, and Joey Maxim.

11. In 1939 and 1940, the flyweight, bantamweight, and middleweight titles were all considered to be vacant in The Ring ratings.

12. In 1929, champions were needed at both ends of the spectrum. Titles were vacant in the flyweight and bantamweight division as well as the light heavyweight and heavyweight divisions.

13. Only during the period from 1962 to 1966 were there five consecutive years in which there were no title vacancies at year end.

14. From 1924 to 1936, one or more classes were lacking a titleholder when The Ring annual ratings were published.

15. In the years 1930 and 1931, Panama Al Brown was champion of the bantamweights and Newsboy Brown, no relation, was the number one-ranked contender. The two Browns met in a nontitle bout in December, 1931, and the Newsboy won a ten-round decision.

16. Because of the confusion created in the middleweight division when the New York Commission and its allied bodies followed the NBA by taking away Paul Pender's world title and designating Dick Tiger of Nigeria as world champion, The Ring in 1962 listed both Pender and Tiger as co-champions.

17. After flyweight champion Pancho Villa's death in 1925, only Izzy Schwartz in 1928, Benny Lynch in 1937, and Peter Kane in 1938 were recognized by The Ring as flyweight champions from 1925 to 1942. In all other years the title was vacant.

18. From 1967 to 1969, Muhammad Ali was heavyweight champion and Joe Frazier was the number one challenger. From 1970 to 1972, Joe Frazier was heavyweight champion and Ali was the number one challenger.

19. From 1924 to 1927, The Ring ratings did not necessarily rate the champion first in his class. In 1924, light heavyweight champion Mike McTigue was rated fourth. In 1925, the fourth-rated bantamweight was Charley Phil Rosenberg, the champion and lightweight champion, Rocky Kansas, was rated third in his class. In 1926, champion Mickey

ANSWERS The Ring Ratings [127]

Walker was the second-rated middleweight and in 1927, featherweight champion Benny Bass was rated number two.

20. The top two rated welterweights in 1934 were Kid Azteca and Bep Van Klavern. Azteca boxed 33 years from 1929 to 1961, while Van Klavern retired early in 1956 at the age of 48 after a 29-year career.

21. Heavyweight Lee Oma, with only six characters in his full name, has the shortest name of all rated boxers.

22. There have been 11 men who were fortunate enough to receive title chances even though they were never rated in the top ten at year end at any point in their careers. Jean-Pierre Coopman, Terry Daniels, Richard Dunn, Buster Mathis, Al McCoy, Tom McNeeley, Jack Roper, Pete Rademacher, Ron Stander, Harry Thomas, and Dave Zyglewicz. Of these men, only Buster Mathis lasted as long as 11 rounds. All of the others were stopped in 6 rounds or less.

23. In 1942, the fifth-ranked heavyweight was Harry Bobo, the sixth was Big Boy Brown, and Turkey Thompson was number three.

24. Paulino Uzcudun boxed Primo Carnera for the heavyweight championship in 1933. Uzcudun was ranked third in 1928, but was unranked from 1929 to 1932.

25. Big John Tate was unranked from 1976 to 1978, but won the WBA heavyweight crown in 1979.

26. Both Archie Moore and Sugar Ray Robinson were ranked in 17 consecutive years from 1945 to 1961. In addition, Moore was also in the ratings in 1940, 1942, 1943 and 1962 and Robinson was rated in 1941, 1942 and 1944.

27. Mimun Ben Ali was the number one challenger in the flyweight division in 1960. He was a top-ranking flyweight and bantamweight from 1958 to 1967. Muhammad Ali was known as Cassius Clay in 1960 and first appeared in the Ring ratings as the ninth-rated heavyweight in 1961.

28. The junior lightweight class was a recognized class from 1924 to 1931. Junior welterweights were also recognized from 1928 to 1931. Both junior classes were resurrected in 1962.

29. Emile (Spider) Pladner was the twelfth-rated flyweight in 1927, eighth flyweight in 1928, ninth bantamweight in 1929, and sixth bantamweight in 1930 and 1931. He won the flyweight title in 1929, but lost it six weeks later.

30. *Luther Rawlings was unranked as late as June, 1951. By August he had jumped to fourth and was number one at year end. In 1952, he lost four of five bouts and by October had dropped out of the top ten. In the 1952 annual ratings, he was only listed as a class A welterweight and was unranked in the top 17 boxers in that class. Rawlings, whose real name was Lucius Minor, Jr., had a 38-25-9 record from 1947 to 1959 and defeated Art Aragon and Virgil Akins.*

31. *The first true "unknown" to appear in the annual ratings was the tenth-ranked heavyweight in 1932—Edward "Unknown" Winston.*

32. *The heavyweight champion in 1972 was Joe Frazier. The number one and number two contenders were Muhammad Ali and George Foreman and the number five contender was Floyd Patterson. All four were also world heavyweight champions at one time in addition to all being Olympic champions.*

33. *Sean O'Grady started boxing professionally at the age of 15 in 1975. After his first two years of boxing he had compiled a record of 42-1. He later became the WBA lightweight champion.*

34. *In 1940, Max Baer was the number one rated heavyweight and his brother Buddy was number six. Twenty years later, the Fullmer brothers, Gene and Don, both appeared among the top ten middleweights. Gene was rated first and Don ninth.*

35. *Tami Mauriello, Jimmy Bivins and Archie Moore share this unusual distinction. In 1940, Moore was number four, Bivins number six, and Mauriello number nine among the middleweights. By 1942, Bivins was the number one heavyweight. Mauriello reached that status in 1946, but Moore had to wait until 1955 before being classed as the number one heavyweight. Ezzard Charles also was rated as a middleweight in 1941 and also later became a number one rated heavyweight.*

36. *Karel Sys, the Belgian heavyweight, was finally given proper recognition in 1951 as the number five heavyweight. He started boxing professionally in 1932, and by the time he made the top ten had compiled a record of 104-10-7 and had been European heavyweight champion for seven years.*

37. *None of the top ten heavyweights had challenged for the title prior to that year. This phenomenon had occurred in five previous years, but has not happened again since 1957.*

Odds and Ends

1. When was the last bout that went more than 15 rounds?
2. As of 1980, when was the last bout that was scheduled for more than 15 rounds?
3. What do King Tut and Babe Ruth have in common with Laverne and Shirley?
4. What two boxers met 14 times with neither one winning a single bout?
5. What are the nationalities of the following boxers: Young Zulu Kid, Frankie Conley, Bushy Graham, Johnny Dundee, Young Corbett III, Joe Grim, and Hugo Corro?
6. Which boxer lost to both Joe Louis and Ray Robinson?
7. What boxer fought 202 consecutive bouts without appearing in the same city for any two bouts in a row?
8. Name the ex-NYU drama student who made a farewell address to the crowd over the ring microphone following his final bout.
9. Who was the first winner of the James J. Walker Award?
10. What modern boxer's career spanned five decades?
11. Who were the tallest boxers to face each other?
12. Who boxed the most rounds in two consecutive bouts?
13. Who knocked out six opponents in one night?
14. Who holds the record for most consecutive bouts against different men named Jimmy?
15. Who boxed three main events in one day in three different locations?

16. Who was knocked down the most times in one bout yet got up to win?

17. What bout, lasting more than one round, produced the most knockdowns per round?

18. What boxer with a record of 7 wins and 43 losses, who was knocked out 30 times, twice defeated a man who twice knocked out a man, who twice defeated a man, who defeated a man, who defeated a welterweight, middleweight, light heavyweight, and heavyweight?

19. For what boxing match was a mattress, jigsaw puzzle, and a Bible accepted in lieu of the admission price?

20. When and where were 113 bouts contested in one day and one place?

21. What NCAA boxing champion became a successful professional football player?

22. Who popularized these punches?
    a. pivot punch
    b. occipital punch
    c. corkscrew punch
    d. aluminum punch
    e. "Mary Ann"
    f. cosmic punch
    g. solar plexus punch

23. What dentist became a professional boxer at the age of 46?

24. Who was the Omnipotent Oom?

25. What boxer quit when his opponent refused to take advantage of him?

26. What boxer knocked out 20 of his opponents, but was himself knocked out 13 times in his 35-bout career?

27. What boxer in 1952 boxed in 17 bouts and had a record of 7-10, yet never won a decision or lost by knockout?

ODDS AND ENDS

28. What champion was a vegetarian?
29. Who invented the first mouthpiece?
30. Who was the Kentucky Rosebud and what was his boxing achievement?
31. Who was Hal Bagwell and why is his name in the record book?
32. What was the first bout where ringside seats sold for $100?
33. What boxers fought a ten-round bout that lasted 11 rounds?
34. What boxer earned $45,000 for his first professional bout?
35. How many rounds was the Peter Jackson-Jim Corbett bout scheduled for? How long did it last?
36. Jackson injured his ankle in training for this bout. How did it happen?
37. Who was the oldest boxer to be known as "Kid"?
38. What man came out of retirement after ten years of inactivity to win a championship?
39. Who defeated Al Jolson and boxed Jackie Cooper in the same year?
40. What middleweight of the 1950s had only 13 knockouts in 97 bouts, yet had 3 consecutive one-round knockouts in less than one month?
41. On September 1, 1920, the New York State Boxing Commission began operations under the Walker Law. This law permitted 15-round bouts to a decision. Who was the first boxer to receive a license under this law?
42. Who had the most consecutive one-round knockouts?
43. When was the first advertised boxing match between women?

44. What two boxers were *both* counted out in a bout that went the distance?
45. Which boxer fought 41 bouts with 12 different champions, yet never boxed in a title bout?
46. What man defeated nine different champions and also never received a title chance?
47. What boxer was elected champion by a poll of boxing fans?
48. One boxer became a dentist in Hollywood after he retired from the ring. Who was he?
49. Who boxed the most draws in his lifetime?

ANSWERS

1. On March 17, 1943, lightweight Bobby Ruffin knocked out Bobby McIntyre in New Orleans in the seventeenth round of a scheduled 20-round bout. There have been four recorded scheduled 20-rounders since then, but the longest of these only lasted 15 rounds.

2. The last bout scheduled for 20 rounds was on June 1, 1971, in Oklahoma City, when Kelly Burden stopped Alonzo Harris in the tenth round of their light heavyweight bout.

3. They met in Milwaukee. On January 28, 1929, in Milwaukee, a boxer, born Henry Tuttle, but using the ring name of King Tut, met someone named Babe Ruth and knocked him out in the first round. Apparently baseball pseudonyms were popular in those days, as one month later, also in Milwaukee, Tut stopped Babe Herman in the fourth round.

4. Packey O'Gatty and Frankie Jerome, bantamweights, faced each other 14 times from September 25, 1915, to September 28, 1917, including five times during March, 1916. Under the Frawley law which was in effect from 1911 to 1917, decisions were not permitted, and, consequently, all 14 of their bouts resulted in a no-decision conclusion, since they all went the distance. Thirteen of the bouts were four rounds and the other was a six-rounder.

5. All were born in Italy except for Corro, who is Argentinian. The others were ring names. Their real names were: Giuseppe Di Melfi, Francesco Conte, Angelo Geraci, Joseph Corrara, Ralph Capabianca Giordano, and Saverio Giannone.

6. Bob Fitzsimmons. In 1967, an NCR-315 computer was programmed to simulated boxing matches. Sixteen heavyweight champions were rated on 58 factors, such as speed, hardness of punch, courage, and susceptibility to cuts. An all-time heavyweight tournament was run using these champions and the results were broadcast in blow by blow recreations of the matches. Fitzsimmons was stopped by Joe Louis in the quarter-finals of this mythical tournament. The radio broadcasts were quite successful and the following year an all-time middleweight championship tournament was run. Fitzsimmons, who held the middleweight championship prior to gaining the heavyweight championship, was also selected for this computer tournament and again lost in the quarter-finals—this time to Ray Robinson.

Results of the All-time Heavyweight Championship Computer Tournament

Jack Dempsey defeated Jim Corbett, knockout seventh round.
John L. Sullivan defeated Jim Braddock, decision.
Joe Louis defeated Jess Willard, knockout fifteenth round.
Bob Fitzsimmons defeated Jack Sharkey, decision.
Max Baer defeated Jack Johnson, decision.
Rocky Marciano defeated Gene Tunney, decision.
Jim Jeffries defeated Joe Walcott, knockout tenth round.
Muhammad Ali defeated Max Schmeling, decision.

Jack Dempsey defeated John L. Sullivan, knockout seventh round.
Joe Louis defeated Bob Fitzsimmons, TKO tenth round.
Rocky Marciano defeated Max Baer, TKO thirteenth round.
Jim Jeffries defeated Muhammad Ali, decision.

Jack Dempsey defeated Joe Louis, decision.
Rocky Marciano defeated Jim Jeffries, TKO fourteenth round.

Rocky Marciano defeated Jack Dempsey, knockout fourteenth round.

Results of the All-Time Middleweight Championship Computer Tournament

Marcel Cerdan defeated Carmen Basilio, knockout fourth round.
Emile Griffith defeated Kid McCoy, decision.
Stanley Ketchel defeated Gene Fullmer, TKO seventh round.
Rocky Graziano defeated Tiger Flowers, knockout eleventh round.
Ray Robinson defeated Jack (Nonpareil) Dempsey, knockout eleventh round.
Bob Fitzsimmons defeated Jake LaMotta, decision.

ANSWERS Odds and Ends [135]

Mickey Walker defeated Dick Tiger, knockout ninth round.
Harry Greb defeated Tony Zale, knockout fourteenth round.

Marcel Cerdan defeated Emile Griffith, knockout tenth round.
Stanley Ketchel defeated Rocky Graziano, knockout eleventh round.
Ray Robinson defeated Bob Fitzsimmons, TKO third round.
Mickey Walker defeated Harry Greb, decision.

Stanley Ketchel defeated Marcel Cerdan, knockout twelfth round.
Ray Robinson defeated Mickey Walker, decision.

Ray Robinson defeated Stanley Ketchel, decision.

7. Young Stribling started his career in Atlanta, Georgia, in 1921. In 1921 and 1922, he fought mainly in Georgia. In May, 1923, he had two consecutive bouts in Atlanta. For the next nine years, from May 17, 1923, until July 15, 1932, he engaged in 202 bouts without appearing in the same city for two straight bouts. His skein was broken during a tour of Australia when he remained in Sydney for two weeks and had bouts on July 4 and 15, 1932. During 1925 he boxed 25 bouts in 24 different cities and in 1928 he boxed 21 bouts in 21 different cities. His traveling schedule was similar to professional basketball teams as he went from Pittsburgh to San Francisco to Augusta, Georgia, to Boston to Kansas City in one stretch in 1925. He boxed in 113 different cities in his 286-bout career. His career was ended in 1933 when he was killed in a motorcycle accident. He boxed in 102 cities in the United States, in 37 different states, and in 11 different cities in 7 foreign countries.

Albany, Ga.
Americus, Ga.
Appleton, Wis.
Atlanta, Ga.
Augusta, Ga.
Bainbridge, Ga.
Baltimore, Md.
Beckley, Va.

Birmingham, Ala.
Boston, Mass.
Brooklyn, N.Y.
Buffalo, N.Y.
Canton, Ohio
Cairo, Ga.
Charleston, S.C.
Charlotte, N.C.

Chattanooga, Tenn.
Chicago, Ill.
Cincinnati, Ohio
Cleveland, Ohio
Colorado Springs, Colo.
Columbia, Ala.
Columbus, Ga.
Columbus, Ohio
Dallas, Texas
Dayton, Ohio
Daytona, Fla.
Des Moines, Ia.
Detroit, Mich.
Dothan, Ala.
Durham, N.C.
El Paso, Texas
Evansville, Ind.
Fayetteville, N.C.
Flint, Mich.
Goldsboro, N.C.
Grand Rapids, Mich.
Greensboro, N.C.
Greenville, Miss.
High Point, N.C.
Houston, Texas
Huntsville, Ala.
Hutchinson, Kans.
Indianapolis, Ind.
Jacksonville, Fla.
Johnson City, Tenn.
Kalamazoo, Mich.
Kansas City, Mo.
Knoxville, Tenn.
Little Rock, Ark.
Los Angeles, Cal.
Louisville, Ky.
Macon, Ga.
Memphis, Tenn.
Meridian, Miss.
Miami, Fla.
Milledgeville, Ga.

Milwaukee, Wis.
Minneapolis, Minn.
Mobile, Ala.
Montgomery, Ala.
Muskogee, Okla.
Nashville, Tenn.
Newark, N.J.
New Haven, Conn.
New Orleans, La.
New York, N.Y.
Norfolk, N.C.
Oklahoma City, Okla.
Omaha, Nebr.
Orlando, Fla.
Pensacola, Fla.
Philadelphia, Pa.
Phoenix, Ariz.
Pittsburgh, Pa.
Portland, Maine
Portland, Oreg.
Quitman, Ga.
Raleigh, N.C.
Rome, Ga.
St. Louis, Mo.
St. Petersburg, Fla.
Salt Lake City, Utah
San Antonio, Tex.
San Francisco, Cal.
Sarasota, Fla.
Savannah, Ga.
Shreveport, La.
Spokane, Wash.
Springfield, Mo.
Tampa, Fla.
Thomasville, Ga.
Topeka, Kans.
Tulsa, Okla.
Valdosta, Ga.
Waterloo, Iowa
West Palm Beach, Fla.
Wichita, Kans.

ANSWERS Odds and Ends [137]

Wilkes Barre, Pa.
Wilmington, Del.
Winston-Salem, N.C.
Youngstown, Ohio

Adelaide, Brisbane,
 Melbourne, Perth, and
 Sydney, Australia

Toronto, Canada
Havana, Cuba
London, England
Paris, France
Matamoras, Mexico
Johannesburg, South Africa

8. Francis (Chico) Vejar, who had studied business administration and drama at New York University in 1951, and who fought 28 nationally televised bouts, closed out his boxing career with a victory over contender Wilfie Greaves at St. Nicholas Arena on March 27, 1961. He received a standing ovation after the bout and responded by making a farewell speech to the crowd. He retired with a record of 93-20-4 and although he never received a title shot he was a top middleweight contender throughout the 1950s. He has since devoted much of his time to raising funds for United Cerebral Palsy.

9. It was none other than Jimmy Walker himself. This award, given by the Boxing Writers' Association of New York, is presented to an individual for long and meritorious service in boxing. From 1940 through 1947 it was simply called the Meritorious Service Award. Other winners include Nat Fleischer, Don Dunphy, and Sam Taub.

10. Kid Azteca, Mexican welterweight and middleweight, began his professional career in 1929 at the age of 14 and fought at least one bout each year until 1961. He won 149, lost 40, and had 9 draws in his recorded bouts. Unlike many boxers towards the end of their careers, he won 7 of his last 8 bouts by knockout and boxed a draw in the other. Jem Mace, Daniel Mendoza, and Tom Faulkner also boxed in five decades during the bareknuckle era. Mace competed from 1855 to 1890, a 35-year span—the longest on record.

11. Big Ben Moroz, 7 feet 1 inch, 302 pounds, and Gilbert Stromquist, 7 feet, 253 pounds, met three times in 1943 and 1944, with Moroz winning all three bouts by knockout. Moroz compiled a record of 20-16-1 from 1939 to 1946. Stromquist won only 5 of 19 during his short (?) career from 1942 to 1945.

12. Lightweight Andy Bowen on April 6, 1893, went 110 rounds against Jack Burke at the Olympic Club in New Orleans in a bout that lasted 7 hours and 19 minutes. This was the longest bout ever fought under the Marquess of Queensberry rules. The bout was called a draw when both fighters were unable to continue. Less than two months later, in his next bout, Bowen defeated Jack Everhardt in 85 rounds, also at the Olympic Club. This is the longest bout to a decision in modern boxing history. For his efforts, Bowen received $2,500 for the Burke bout and $2,000 for the Everhardt bout.

13. Lamar Clark, heavyweight from Cedar City, Utah, stopped five opponents in 1 round each and stopped the sixth in 2 rounds on December 1, 1958, in Bingham, Utah. Three nights previously he stopped two men in 2 rounds each and knocked out another on the following night for a total of 9 knockouts in 12 rounds in four nights. On three other occasions in his career he stopped two men in one night and on another occasion he stopped three men in one night. In 1958, he won 31 consecutive bouts by knockout and extended his streak to 44 consecutive knockouts before he was kayoed in 9 rounds on national television by Bartolo Soni on April 8, 1960. In his next bout he was stopped by Pete Rademacher in the tenth round and after a two-round knockout victory he was stopped by Cassius Clay in the second round. He retired from the ring in 1961 with a lifetime record of 47-3-1 and 45 knockouts, 30 of them in the first-round.

14. Ernie Durando, Bayonne, N.J., middleweight, achieved this unusual distinction in 1949 when his last six bouts that year were against Jimmy Taylor, Jimmy Milligan, Jimmy Snedeker, Jimmy Flood, Jimmy Mills and Jimmy Sanders. He knocked out four of the Jimmys, was knocked out by Flood and lost a decision to Taylor.

15. Battling Levinsky on January 1, 1915, boxed a ten-round no-decision bout in Brooklyn against Bartley Madden in the morning, another 10-round no-decision bout with Soldier Kearns in New York in the afternoon, and a 12-round no-decision bout with Gunboat Smith in Waterbury, Connecticut in the evening. But why would anyone want to attend a boxing match on New Year's morning?

16. Joe Jeanette, heavyweight, got up off the canvas 27 times in a bout with Sam McVey in Paris on April 17, 1909. McVey was down "only" 11 times but was finally stopped in the 49th round. Only four others were ever down more times in one bout, but all four lost.

17. On September 7, 1925 in Buenos Aires, Argentina, Vittorio Campolo knocked down Miguel (The Human Yo-Yo) Ferrara 36 times in 5 rounds for an average of more than seven knockdowns per round, or a knockdown less than every 25 seconds.

ANSWERS Odds and Ends

18. Joey Blair, an Akron middleweight who got knocked out twice a year on the average from 1962 to 1978, had a hot streak in 1970 and defeated Primus Williams twice in November. Williams had a career record of 6-25, but two of his six victories were knockouts over Gene Masters just one month prior to his meeting Blair.

Masters only won 6 of his 14 bouts, but two of his wins were against Tommy Shaffer in 1969. Shaffer's record was 11 wins and 27 losses but in his third pro bout he defeated Doyle Baird.

That was only Baird's sixth pro bout and he later became a ranked contender and boxed a draw with middleweight champion Nino Benvenuti in a non-title bout, and also defeated Don Fullmer. Fullmer was WBA middleweight champion earlier in his career and had defeated Emile Griffith, Virgil Akins, Bobo Olson and Jimmy Ellis, who became WBA heavyweight champion in 1968.

So in a roundabout way Joey Blair can claim that just five men stood between him and the heavyweight championship of the world.

19. On Friday, March 3, 1933, a special bank holiday of indefinite duration was declared by the Governor of New York State due to the country's economic crisis. The 1933 New York Golden Gloves semi-finals were scheduled for St. Nicholas Arena on Monday and Tuesday, March 6 and 7th. Since cash money was scarce, the Daily News, the tournament's sponsor, announced that a barter system would be employed for unreserved seats for the semi-finals. Any goods valued at 50¢ or more would be accepted along with 5¢ in cash to cover the admissions tax. The plan turned out to be a huge success, with over 1,000 people bringing such varied items as hats, coats, overcoats, fish, steaks, chops, potatoes, canned foods, jigsaw puzzles, toilet paper, razor blades, a Bible, a mattress and many other assorted goods. All goods were donated to various charities and the standing-room-only crowds enjoyed two nights of excellent amateur boxing for nominal cost. Boxers appearing on those nights included Gus Lesnevich and Bob Pastor.

20. The first Eastern Tournament of Champions Golden Gloves was held on Washington's Birthday, February 22, 1937, with afternoon and evening cards at Madison Square Garden. Admissions ranged from 40¢ to 75¢ for the 1:00 P.M. to 5:00 P.M. show and 55¢ to $2.20 for the 8:00 P.M. to midnight show. The ads read "A penny a bout—100 punches a minute." This was not an exaggeration. Three rings were used and bouts were held simultaneously. Fifty-seven bouts were contested in the afternoon and 56 more at night. A spectator could have watched 113 bouts for 95¢ over an eight-hour period before going home to rest his eyeballs. Fifteen thousand two hundred and twenty-one people showed up in the afternoon and 17,211 were there for the evening show. This attendance of 17,211 exceeded any other Madison Square Garden boxing show for the remainder of 1937, including professional boxing cards featuring Henry Armstrong, Tony Canzoneri, Kid Chocolate, Max Schmeling, and Max Baer.

21. The 1950 heavyweight NCAA boxing champion was Chuck Drazenovich of Penn State who became a linebacker for the Washington Redskins during the 1950s.

22. a. George LaBlanche used this punch to knock out Jack Dempsey, the Nonpareil, in 1889. LaBlanche swung on his left heel and with his left arm held out straight and stiff, let go to the jaw. The punch has since been ruled illegal.
  b. Edward (Gunboat) Smith called his punch "the flopper," but since this looping right hand aimed at the chin more often landed on the back of the head, it was renamed the occipital punch—or as he called it, the " 'ospital punch."
  c. Kid McCoy used this punch to inflict punishment. He twisted his wrist just before the fist reached the point of contact to gain leverage and cutting power.
  d. This is another name for a low blow.
  e. Frank Moran, one of the "white hopes," called his right hand by this name.
  f. Lou Nova used this name to confuse his opponents. Together with his "dynamic stance" it was to be used to defeat Joe Louis. It didn't help; Louis stopped him in the sixth round.
  g. Bob Fitzsimmons was best known for this punch as he used it to knock out Jim Corbett and win the heavyweight title. Many boxers dating back to Jack Broughton were aware of the effectiveness of this blow, but Fitzsimmons has received the most credit.

23. Dr. Herbert Odom, a professional dentist, decided to try his hand at pro boxing in 1979 at the age of 46. He was the NCAA welterweight champion in 1954 and 1955 while attending Michigan State University.

24. The Omnipotent Oom was a yogi that Lou Nova hired to help him prepare for his bout with Joe Louis. He created the "dynamic stance" and the "cosmic punch" that were supposed to help Nova

ANSWERS Odds and Ends [141]

overcome Louis. But they didn't—Louis knocked out Nova in the sixth round.

25. Sugar Ray Robinson scored 109 knockouts in his career, but the strangest was one that was recorded against Jan De Bruin in Antwerp, Belgium, in 1951. In the middle of the eighth round, De Bruin suddenly parted the ropes and strolled back to his dressing room. After the bout De Bruin stated that he asked no quarter from any man in the ring and that Robinson had spared him on several occasions. He complained that Ray refused to take advantage of openings, so he quit.

26. Dave Landers, an Australian lightweight from 1946 to 1952, engaged in 35 bouts and either knocked out his opponent or was himself knocked out in all but two of them.

27. A Nigerian lightweight, Dan Collie, compiled this unusual record. He won seven bouts all by knockout, and lost ten bouts, all by decision.

28. Freddy Welsh, the lightweight champion from 1914 to 1917, was a vegetarian and later operated a "health farm."

29. A London dentist named Jack Marks developed the first mouthpiece or gumshield. Ted (Kid) Lewis became the first to use one on a regular basis.

30. The Kentucky Rosebud was a top featherweight during the 1890s. In February, 1916, he knocked out John Henry Johnson in four rounds in Philadelphia. What made this achievement remarkable was that the Rosebud was 63 years old at the time while Johnson was a mere 45. He is the oldest man to win a bout by knockout.

31. Hal Bagwell is credited with being undefeated in 180 consecutive bouts from 1938 to 1948. Included in that streak were only 5 draws. Second to Bagwell on the all-time list is Packy McFarland, with 97 consecutive bouts without a loss.

32. The Corbett-Sullivan title bout on September 7, 1892, was the first heavyweight championship with tickets priced at $100 apiece for front row seats, but the Peter Jackson-James J. Corbett bout—one year earlier on May 21, 1891—was the first in which front row seats were priced at $100. Since only club members could attend this bout, all other tickets were sold for payment of one year's club membership dues of $66 50.

33. On August 22, 1946, Bernard Docusen and Henry Jordon had completed the first round of their 10-round bout at Ebbets Field, Brooklyn, New York, when a heavy downfall washed out the show. When they resumed action the following night, the bout was restarted and Docusen won a ten-round decision, although it took him 11 rounds.

34. Ed "Too-Tall" Jones received $45,000 for a six-round bout against Yaqui Meneses in Las Cruces, New Mexico, on November 3, 1979. Jones established a record for most money paid to a 6-foot 9-inch ex-pro football player for a six-round bout. Through 1980, this was also the most money paid to any boxer for his first professional bout. In contrast, Joe Louis, Floyd Patterson, and Rocky Marciano did not receive more than $75 for their first bouts and Tommy Burns received only $1.25 for his first bout in 1900.

35. Peter Jackson and James J. Corbett agreed to a fight to a finish with gloves under the Marquess of Queensberry rules for their bout in San Francisco in 1891. The bout ended after the sixty-first round—one in which neither boxer threw a punch. The referee was satisfied that neither was capable of fighting any longer and declared the bout a draw.

36. Jackson injured his ankle when he fell from a tree while training for the bout. While doing roadwork, he was chased by a dog, and neither wanting to hurt the dog nor get bitten, he climbed a tree. While climbing down he lost his grip and fell on his ankle.

37. Luis Villanueva Paramo was known as Kid Azteca when he began his professional boxing career at the age of 14 in 1929. When he retired from the ring in 1961 at the age of 46, he was still known as "Kid" Azteca, although "Gramps" would have been more appropriate.

38. Welshman Tommy Farr was a top rated boxer who lost a 15-round decision to Joe Louis for the world heavyweight championship in 1937. He retired from the ring in 1940 and after ten years of inactivity, attempted a comeback in 1950. He won the Welsh heavyweight title in 1951 and retired permanently in 1953 at the age of 39. He won 11 of 16 bouts from 1950 to 1953.

39. In 1944, welterweight Tommy Bell won a ten-round bout from a boxer who called himself Al Jolson. Later that year, Bell met a boxer named Jackie Cooper in a bout that was called no contest after eight rounds.

ANSWERS Odds and Ends [143]

40. Holley Mims was never known for his knockout punch. He boxed 27 pro bouts before scoring his first knockout. After his thirtieth bout he only had this one knockout to his credit, yet in his next three bouts, from April 23, 1951, through May 16, 1951, he knocked out three opponents in the first round. He never again scored a one-round knockout.

41. The first license was granted to the heavyweight champion Jack Dempsey. The next eight licenses were granted to the eight boxers appearing at Madison Square Garden in the initial show on September 17, 1920. Johnny Dundee and Joe Welling headlined the main event at that show.

42. A boxer with the appropriate name of "One-Round" Hogan was credited with 18 consecutive knockouts in the first round in 1910. Young Otto scored 16 in a row in 1905.

43. In June, 1722, only three years after Jim Figg popularized boxing, the following advertisement appeared in a London paper:
"Challenge—I, Elizabeth Wilkinson of Clerkenwell, having had some words with Hannah Hyfield, and requiring satisfaction, do invite her to meet me upon the stage and to box for three guineas; each woman holding half a crown in each hand and the first woman that drops the money to lose the battle."
The answer to the challenge was also printed in the paper:
"I, Hannah Hyfield of Newgate Market, hearing of the resoluteness of Elizabeth Wilkinson, will not fail, God willing, to give her more blows than words; I ask from her no favor and she may expect a good thumping."
The bout, however, was never put on. The police also saw the ad and advised the women that they would be incarcerated if they attempted to fight.

44. In Zagreb, Yugoslavia, December 20, 1968, Yvan Prebeg and Blas Di Vanbode both landed knockout punches simultaneously and were both counted out in the fourth round. The referee ordered them to resume boxing when they had both finally arisen and the bout went the full ten rounds. Appropriately it resulted in a decision of a draw.

45. Soldier Bartfield, a Brooklyn lightweight and welterweight from 1912 to 1925, met Jack Britton, Harry Greb, Johnny Dundee, Ted (Kid) Lewis, Benny Leonard, Al McCoy, Mike O'Dowd, Billy Papke, Dave Rosenberg, Jimmy Slattery, Mickey Walker, and Johnny Wilson, champions all. Thirty-five of the 41 bouts were no-decision bouts; Bartfield defeated Papke and lost to Britton, Leonard, Slattery, and Rosenberg. He also boxed a draw with Rosenberg.

46. Lloyd Marshall, a middleweight and light heavyweight during the 1940s, also boxed 12 champions, but his record was 9-8 against them. He defeated Ken Overlin, Babe Risko, Teddy Yarosz, Ezzard Charles, Joey Maxim, Anton Christoforidis, Lou Brouillard, Jake La Motta, and Freddy Mills. He also boxed Ceferino Garcia, Archie Moore, and Bobo Olson. Although he had a lifetime record of 64-24-2 from 1937 to 1951, he never received a title shot.

47. Promoter Mike Collins founded a boxing publication called The Boxing Blade in 1919. It established the junior welterweight division. Subscribers to the magazine were entitled to vote for the champion of this division and they elected Pinkey Mitchell as the first junior welterweight champion. Mitchell boxed mostly in no-decision bouts in his career from 1917 to 1927, and of his 79 recorded contests he is credited with only 12 victories and 12 losses—the rest being no-decision or draws.

48. Dr. Louis C. Wallach, a successful New York and Hollywood dentist, was known to boxing fans from 1906 to 1921 as lightweight contender Leach Cross. He competed in 155 bouts and lost only 10.

49. Matty Baldwin, a Boston lightweight from 1902 to 1914, engaged in 185 recorded bouts and drew in 49 of them. He also had 34 no-decision bouts, won 77, and lost 25.